THE ESSENCE OF

NEURAL NETWORKS

THE ESSENCE OF COMPUTING SERIES

Published Titles
The Essence of Program Design
The Essence of Discrete Mathematics
The Essence of Logic
The Essence of Programming Using C++
The Essence of Artificial Intelligence
The Essence of Databases
The Essence of Human–Computer Interaction
The Essence of Structured Systems Analysis Techniques
The Essence of Neural Networks

Forthcoming titles
The Essence of Z
The Essence of Compilers
The Essence of Professional Issues in Computing

THE ESSENCE OF

NEURAL NETWORKS

Robert Callan
Southampton Institute

Prentice Hall Europe
LONDON   NEW YORK   TORONTO   SYDNEY   TOKYO
SINGAPORE   MADRID   MEXICO CITY   MUNICH   PARIS

First published 1999 by
Prentice Hall Europe
Campus 400, Maylands Avenue
Hemel Hempstead
Hertfordshire, HP2 7EZ
A division of
Simon & Schuster International Group

Typeset in 10/12pt Times
by Aarontype Limited, Bristol

Printed and bound in Great Britain by
Biddles Ltd, Guildford

Library of Congress Cataloging-in-Publication Data

Callan, Robert.
    The essence of neural networks / Robert Callan.
        p.   cm. – (The essence of computing series)
    Includes bibliographical references and index.
    ISBN 0-13-908732-X (alk. paper)
        1. Neural networks (Computer science)   I. Title.   II.   Series.
    QA76.87.C35   1998
    006.3'2–dc21
                                                        98-27559
                                                        CIP

British Library Cataloguing in Publication Data

A catalogue record for this book is available from
the British Library
ISBN: 0-13-908732-X

1 2 3 4 5   03 02 01 00 99

Contents

Preface

Think for a moment about a number of tasks that you perform daily. You are sitting at an office desk when a male colleague walks into the room wearing a new hat and looking somewhat younger, having shaved his beard. Would you still recognize him? No doubt you would, because his intention is not to deceive you. He asks you: 'Do you have my book you borrowed yesterday?'. You remember the book and interpret the request as asking for the book to be returned. You look at the desk, and resting on top of a box containing diskettes is a pile of papers with the book in the middle. You reach out for the book without being conscious of the need to direct your arm. You move the papers, grasp the book and hand it to your colleague.

These daily tasks are effortless, and yet each one would appear to involve many computational steps. We would look in awe at a machine performing with such competence. You could imagine the scale of the task, programming a computer-based system to recognize faces and other objects that can appear in different contexts, to understand requests for action, to plan robotic movements, etc. In a bid to solve such complicated tasks, many scientists have turned their attention to machines that have a resemblance to our own computer, the brain. These machines, with their networks of simple processing elements, are proving to be adaptable to a wide range of tasks; they are known as neural networks. Neural networks are not programmed as such, but learn how to perform a task

Neural networks have proved to be very good at pattern recognition tasks such as recognizing underwater objects from sonar returns or the detection of credit card fraud. Commercial applications that use neural networks are emerging all the time. There is also a growing research base for applying neural networks to what are known as high-level cognitive tasks, such as natural language understanding or planning the actions of some autonomous vehicle. These high-level tasks have for many years come under the discipline of artificial intelligence (AI). There is now a new form of AI, which seeks to integrate ideas from 'traditional AI' and the field of neural networks. This 'new AI' would appear to have a great deal of potential for propelling computer-based systems into the next generation.

This book is designed to be a first course on neural networks for undergraduate students. Most neural network books assume that the student has a good grounding in mathematics. While it is not possible to avoid mathematics completely, this book attempts to keep the maths to its minimum; in the main, maths is used for the concise presentation of algorithms. Even if the level of maths presented still appears daunting, the reader is encouraged to work through the many examples and to see how these examples relate to the notation. While the book's main aim is to cover the basic concepts, the key neural network models that are introduced are covered to a depth that should allow competent programmers to implement these networks in a language of their choice.

The first six chapters cover what could be considered to be the main neural network models that are essential for a fundamental grounding in the subject. These six chapters occupy just over two-thirds of the text. It would have been tempting to expand the mathematical notation and the algorithms in these chapters but it was felt that this could deter the reader. Instead, the presentation in some parts is deliberately concise, with reliance on expansion through examples. For instance, probably the most daunting algorithm presented in this book is the backpropagation algorithm in Chapter 2, and yet this algorithm is very simple when put into practice. Therefore, some short examples are followed by a more developed example at the end of the chapter. The reader should also refer to Appendix A for a brief reminder of linear algebra and for an elaboration of some of the notation used in Chapter 2. The last two chapters are devoted to an overview of some of the links that are developing between neural networks and traditional AI. Chapter 7 is really a preparation for Chapter 8. There is growing interest in the synthesis of neural networks and traditional AI. In contrast to the first six chapters, Chapter 8 does not aim to equip the reader with knowledge that will find an immediate application. Indeed, a number of the concepts introduced might appear difficult and somewhat abstract. The introduction of this material gives us an opportunity to present some work in which modular network systems are being used to tackle some difficult computing problems. The development of future neural network models will be pursued on a number of frontiers but certainly we will learn a great deal in the drive to tackle the sort of tasks that fall within the domain of traditional artificial intelligence. The reader should be prepared to revisit Chapter 8 every so often, but above all the reader is encouraged to explore the referenced texts.

The book is supported by a site on the World Wide Web located at

http://www.solent.ac.uk/syseng/faculty/html/staff/rcallan/essnn

There is neural net software that can be downloaded from this site.

R. Callan

Acknowledgements

I would like to thank Dominic Palmer-Brown for some useful comments on Chapters 7 and 8. Thanks to John Flackett for comments on various chapters and for providing the explanatory diagram of a recursive autoassociative memory in Chapter 8. Thanks to Dave Parsons, as someone new to the field, for useful comments on the first two chapters. Thanks also to Hesham Azzam who has been a supportive colleague over the years. Finally, I would like to thank the reviewers for some useful suggestions on an early draft of this text and Jackie Harbor of Prentice Hall for her help and support.

CHAPTER 1

Introduction

Aim: To introduce the basic elements of a neural network.

Objectives: You should be able to:

> describe in simple terms what a neural network is;
> define the terms unit, weight and activation function;
> describe a network's connections in matrix form;
> explain in simple terms what is involved when a network learns.

1.1 Introduction

Artificial neural networks are parallel computing devices consisting of many interconnected simple processors. These processors are quite simplistic, especially when compared with the type of processor found in a computer. Each processor in a network is only aware of signals it periodically receives and the signal it periodically sends to other processors, and yet such simple local processors are capable of performing complex tasks when placed together in a large network of orchestrated cooperation.

Artificial neural networks have their roots in work performed in the early part of the twentieth century, but only during the 1990s, after the breaking of some theoretical barriers and the growth in available computing power, have these networks been widely accepted as useful tools. The word 'artificial' is sometimes used to make it clear that discussion is about an artificial device and not about the real biological neural networks found in humans. It is the human brain that has inspired the creation of artificial neural networks and no doubt will influence further development. However, in comparison to the human brain, artificial neural networks are at present highly simplistic abstractions. It is common to drop the prefix 'artificial' when it is clear in which context these networks are being discussed. Also, artificial neural networks are often referred to as connectionist networks when computing ability is emphasized rather than biological fidelity. In other words, connectionists aim to make neural networks solve a task rather than attempt to mimic faithfully some part of a biological process.

1

Although neural networks can be (and are) implemented as fast hardware devices, much research is performed using a conventional computer running software simulations. Software simulation provides a somewhat cheap and flexible environment in which to research ideas and for many real-world applications simulation provides adequate performance. For example, a neural network software package might be used to develop a system for credit scoring of an individual who is applying for a bank loan. Although a neural network solution might have the look and feel of any conventional piece of software, there is a key difference in that most neural solutions are 'learnt' and not programmed: the network learns to perform a task rather than being directly programmed. Indeed, many neural network solutions exist either because it is impossible to write a program or because the neural network 'learnt solution' provides improved performance. For example, as a human expert on house sales, you have a good idea, from experience, what factors influence the selling price of a house, but often there are other more subtle factors involved which might be difficult to convey to a programmer. A selling agency may wish to have a 'neural network price predictor' that has learnt, from many examples of house sales, what factors influence the selling price and the relative importance of these factors. What is more, the neural solution is flexible in that the system can further improve its prediction with experience and can adapt to market influences.

Neural network solutions are growing more sophisticated and no doubt in the coming years our skills for engineering these computing devices will improve. Already, though, there is a vast array of exciting developments. The application base for neural networks is enormous: credit card fraud detection, stock market forecasting, credit scoring, optical character recognition, human health monitoring and diagnosis, machine health monitoring, road vehicle autopilots, learning to land damaged aircraft, etc. Future artificial neural networks will be inspired by further understanding of the human brain, but there is mutual support in that artificial neural networks are being used as models for brain processes to assist in our understanding of the human brain.

The future for neural networks is bright and it is certainly a field that all computer scientists should have some understanding of, as should many other engineers and other scientists.

1.2 The basic components

A neural network is a collection of units that are connected in some pattern to allow communication between the units. These units, also referred to as *neurons* or *nodes*, are simple processors whose computing ability is typically restricted to a rule for combining input signals and an activation rule that takes the combined input to calculate an output signal. Output signals may be sent to other units along connections known as *weights*. The weights usually excite

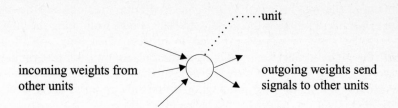

Figure 1.1 A single network unit.

or inhibit the signal that is being communicated. A neural network unit is illustrated in Figure 1.1.

One of the intriguing aspects of neural networks is that although they have units with very limited computing capability, when many of these units are connected together, the complete network is capable of performing a complicated task (see Figure 1.2).

The pattern of connectivity refers to a network's wiring detail: that is, the detail of which units connect, their direction of connection and the values of their weighted connections. The task that a network knows (or its program) is coded in the weights that connect units. The connection pattern is usually determined by a two-stage process: first, the system designer specifies which units are connected and in which direction; and secondly, the weight values are learnt during a training phase.

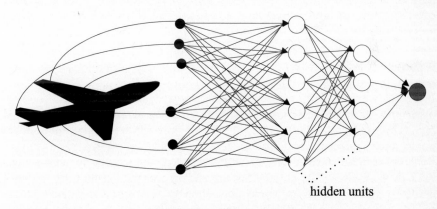

hidden units

● input units taking data from strain gauges

● single output unit in this case indicates
the health of the aircraft

Figure 1.2 Application of a neural network to aircraft health monitoring. Weights are shown connecting units. The input units are taking readings directly from onboard sensors. The output unit indicates the health of the aircraft.

Sometimes the weights can be determined without training, but the great appeal of neural networks is their ability to learn a task from using the kind of data that the network will be expected to process when fully operational. Indeed, for many applications training is the only option for programming a network because we do not have the task-solving knowledge that permits a more traditional form of programming; often the only option is to see whether a network can learn to solve the task at hand.

There are many different types of neural network, but a number of features that are common to all those included in this text can be abstracted:

- a set of simple processing units;
- a pattern of connectivity;
- a rule for propagating signals through the network;
- a rule for combining input signals;
- a rule for calculating an output signal;
- a learning rule to adapt the weights.

A set of simple processing units

Each processing unit usually has incoming weights to receive signals from other network units and outgoing weights to transmit signals to other network units. Some units exist to receive signals from the environment (known as *input units*) and other units exist to communicate back to the environment the result of computation (known as *output units*). Any computing machine has input devices such as a keyboard to receive data from the environment and output devices such as a monitor to display the result of computation. For the purpose of simulation, the input units are often fed pre-processed data from a file and do not connect directly to the environment.

A pattern of connectivity

The pattern of connectivity refers to the way in which the units are connected. In one network model (i.e., type of network) each unit may connect to every other unit; in another network model units may be arranged into an ordered hierarchy of layers where connections are only allowed between units in immediately adjacent layers; other network models allow feedback connections between adjacent layers, or within a layer, or for units to send signals back to themselves. The possibilities are endless, but it is usual for a network model to specify the type of connections allowed. A weight is specified by three parameters: the unit the weight connects from; the unit the weight connects to; and a number (usually real) that denotes the weight value. A negative weight value will inhibit the activity of the connected-to unit, whilst a positive weight value will serve to excite the connected-to unit. The absolute weight value specifies the strength of the connection.

The pattern of connectivity is conveniently described in a matrix, $\mathbf{W}$, where the entry w_{ij} represents the weight value from unit i to unit j (note that in many

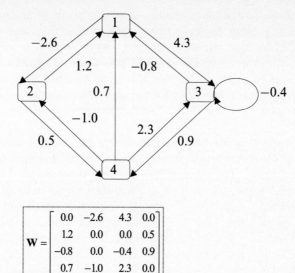

Figure 1.3 The matrix describes the networks' connections. For example, the weight that connects unit 3 (row 3) with unit 1 (column 1) is denoted by $w_{31} = -0.8$.

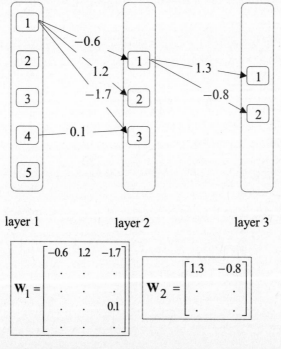

Figure 1.4 The matrices describe the networks' connections. There is a separate matrix for each layer of weights.

texts, the matrix is written so that connections go from unit j to unit i: the important thing is to be consistent when performing matrix and vector operations). More than one weight matrix may be used to describe the pattern of connectivity where units are grouped into layers. Figures 1.3 and 1.4 give examples of the connectivity pattern written as matrices.

The weight matrix is the network's memory that holds the knowledge of how to perform a task.

A rule for controlling the propagation of signals through the network
Conventional computer programs impose conditions on when certain processes can start and finish. The same is true for neural networks. For a particular network model some rule will exist to control when units can be updated (i.e., combine input signals and calculate an output signal) and when a signal can be sent on to other units. With some network models a unit is selected at random for updating, while with other models one group of units must update before another group can be updated.

A rule for combining input signals
It is typical for the incoming signals to a unit to be combined by summing their weighted values. This summation method is illustrated in Figure 1.5, where net_j is the resultant combined input to unit j, x_i is the output from unit i and n is the

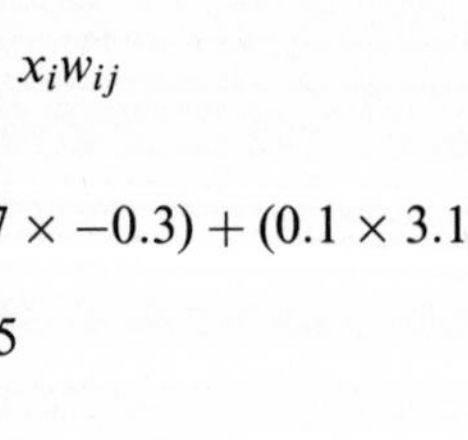

$$net_j = \sum_{i=1}^{n} x_i w_{ij}$$

$$net_j = (0.7 \times -0.3) + (0.1 \times 3.1) + (0.3 \times 0.5)$$

$$= 0.25$$

or, alternatively, in vector notation

$$[0.7 \quad 0.1 \quad 0.3] \begin{bmatrix} -0.3 \\ 3.1 \\ 0.5 \end{bmatrix} = 0.25$$

Figure 1.5 A typical way of summing the signals impinging on a unit.

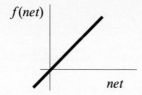

Figure 1.6 The activation is the same as the net input. Note that *f(net)* refers to the activation.

number of impinging connections. Other forms of summation exist, and another typically used method is to square the difference between the strength of a weight and the signal it is carrying and then to sum all of these differences for all weights feeding into a unit.

A rule for calculating an output signal
Units have a rule for calculating an output value that will be transmitted to other units or for presenting to the environment (if an output unit) the end result of computation. This rule is known as an *activation function* and the output value is referred to as the *activation* for the unit. The activation may be: a real number, a real number that is restricted to some interval such as [0, 1], or a discrete number such as $\{0, 1\}$ or $\{+1, -1\}$. The value passed to the activation function is the net combined input to a unit. Some activation functions are given next.

Identity function
The activation function for input units is the identity function, which simply means that the activation (signal sent on to other units) is the same as the net input (Figure 1.6). Input units really serve to distribute input signals to other network units, and so we want the signal coming out of the unit to be the same as that going in. Unlike other network units, input units only have one input value. For instance, an input unit might take a signal from a single sensor placed on the structure of an aircraft. This single input unit has connections to many other units and so the recording from a single sensor gets distributed to other network units. Because input units only serve to distribute signals from the environment, many authors do not consider input units to be part of a neural network.

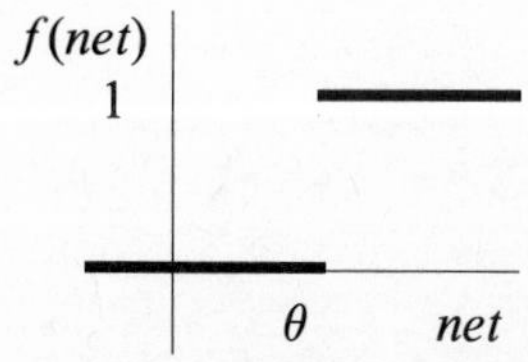

$$f(net) = \begin{cases} 1 & \text{if } net \geq \theta \\ 0 & \text{if } net < \theta \end{cases}$$

Figure 1.7 Binary threshold function.

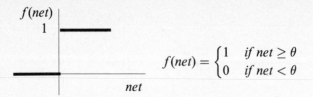

$$f(net) = \begin{cases} 1 & \text{if } net \geq \theta \\ 0 & \text{if } net < \theta \end{cases}$$

Figure 1.8 Binary threshold function with bias term added in.

Binary threshold function

Most network models rely on a nonlinear activation function. A binary threshold function will limit the activation to 1 or 0 depending on the net input relative to some threshold θ (Figure 1.7).

Usually it is more convenient to subtract the threshold (known as a *bias*) from the net input and change the threshold to its mathematical equivalent form, shown in Figure 1.8. The bias w_0 is the negative of the threshold, and in this case the net input is calculated as

$$net_j = w_0 + \sum_{i=1}^{n} x_i w_{ij}$$

The bias is normally thought of as a weight coming from a unit that always has an activation of 1 as shown in Figure 1.9. The net input can be expressed as

$$net_j = \sum_{i=0}^{n} x_i w_{ij}$$

where x_0 always has a value of 1.

Sigmoid function

The sigmoid function is a commonly used activation function. The output from a sigmoid function falls in a continuous range from 0 to 1. An example is the

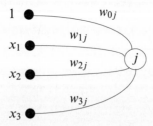

Figure 1.9 For convenience of implementation, the bias term is often thought of as being a weight that is connected to a unit in the previous layer with an activation permanently set to 1.

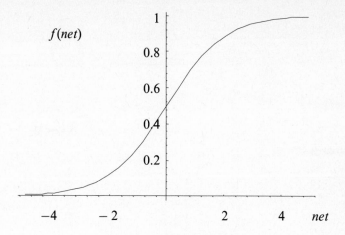

Figure 1.10. The sigmoid function.

logistic function shown in Figure 1.10:

$$f(net) = \frac{1}{1 + \exp(-net)}$$

The slope and output range of the logistic function can vary. The bipolar sigmoid, for example, has an output ranging from -1 to 1.

EXAMPLE 1.1

The following example brings together some of the points discussed so far. The network to be examined knows the XOR relationship. The XOR relationship maps two binary inputs to 0 or 1; the definition is given in Table 1.1. The network model is shown in Figure 1.11, which is a layered feedforward network with two input units, two hidden units and one output unit. *Feedforward* means that connections only travel in one direction from the input layer to the output layer. The *hidden* units are so called because they do not take direct input from the environment or

Table 1.1 *Definition of XOR*

Input		Output
x_1	x_2	
1	1	0
1	0	1
0	1	1
0	0	0

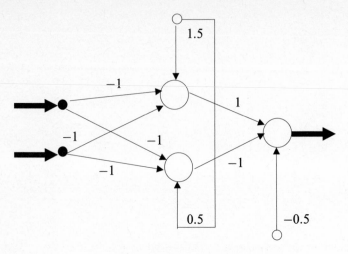

Figure 1.11 Network used in Example 1.1.

send information directly out to the environment. In this example we can think of the environment simply as ourselves feeding values to the input units and monitoring the result via the output units. The units are arranged in layers: the input layer containing the input units, the hidden layer containing the hidden units and the output layer containing the output units. The number of units in each layer depends on the problem being solved and we will discuss this when we take a more in-depth look at feedforward networks in Chapter 2; for the moment, we simply observe that the number of input units matches the number of input values for a pattern and the number of output units the number of output values for a pattern. For this example the net input is calculated according to

$$net_j = \sum_{i=0}^{n} x_i w_{ij}$$

and the output will be calculated using the threshold function

$$f(net) = \begin{cases} 1 & \text{if } net \geq 0 \\ 0 & \text{if } net < 0 \end{cases}$$

Remember that the activation is the same as the net input for units in the input layer. Signals propagate through the network from the input layer to the output layer, and so for a particular input pattern the order of processing is

input layer → hidden layer → output layer

The input will be the first pattern in Table 1.1, which is [1 1]. For the first hidden unit with a bias of 1.5:

$$net = (x_0 \times 1.5) + (x_1 \times -1) + (x_2 \times -1)$$
$$= (1 \times 1.5) + (1 \times -1) + (1 \times -1) = -0.5$$

so the output is 0. For the second hidden unit with a bias of 0.5:

$$net = (x_0 \times 0.5) + (x_1 \times -1) + (x_2 \times -1)$$
$$= (1 \times 0.5) + (1 \times -1) + (1 \times -1) = -1.5$$

so the output is 0. For the output unit with a bias of −0.5:

$$net = (x_0 \times -0.5) + (x_1 \times 1) + (x_2 \times -1)$$
$$= (1 \times -0.5) + (0 \times 1) + (0 \times -1) = -0.5$$

so the output is 0. If the procedure is followed for the other three patterns, the output of the network will match the output column in Table 1.1.

A learning rule to adapt the weights

One of the most attractive features of neural networks is that learning rules exist so that a network can be programmed in an automated way. For example, a function could be written that implements the XOR definition given earlier:

```
int XOR(int val_1, int val_2)
{
     if (val_1 == 1&& val_2 == 1)
         return 0;
     if (value_1 == 0 && val_2 == 0)
         return 0;
     if (val_1 == 1 && val_2 == 0)
         return 1;
     if (val_1 == 0 && val_2 == 1)
        return 1;
}
```

The above code is not particularly efficient and could be implemented in another way. As we have seen, the network given in Example 1.1 implements the same function. The correct operation of this XOR network is dependent on the arrangement of units, the choice of activation function and the weights. The arrangement of units is usually fixed at the start of learning, and so is the choice of activation function. The task during learning then is to adapt the weights so as to produce the desired response.

A common form of learning is supervised learning, where for every input pattern that is presented to the network during training there is a target output

Figure 1.12 A single weight connecting two units. The signal *x* is multiplied by the weight *w*. The output unit has the identity function for its activation function, which means that the output *y* is the same as the weighted input.

pattern. In other words, for any input pattern we know what the output should be. It is usual for the weights to be set to small random values at the start of training and so when an input pattern is presented for the first time it is unlikely that the network will produce the correct output. This discrepancy between what the network actually outputs and what it is required to output constitutes an error, and this error, can be used to adapt the weights. An example of an error-correcting rule is the delta rule or Widrow–Hoff rule. Consider Figure 1.12, where the output unit has an activation (i.e., output) of *y* and a target output *t*. The error, δ, is given by

$$\delta = t - y$$

The signal coming into the output unit is *x*. The delta rule states that the adjustment to be made, Δw, is

$$\Delta w = \eta \delta x$$

where η is a real number known as the *learning rate*. The new weight is then the adjustment added to the old weight

$$w = w + \Delta w$$

A generalized version of the delta rule is used in a learning algorithm presented in Chapter 2 to train networks to perform learning tasks such as the XOR.

At the start of training, the weights are set to small random values; for instance, in the range [−0.3, +0.3]. During training, input pattern after input pattern is presented to the network and weights are continually adapted until for any input the error drops to an acceptable low value. Upon completion of training, the network is tested on data that were not presented during training: testing measures how well the network performs on data it has not seen during training.

1.3 Training a neural net

The performance of a neural network is critically dependent on the training data. The training data must be representative of the task to be learnt.

Training often appears to be an *ad hoc* process in that most problems require much experimentation before acceptable results are attained. The designer of a neural network solution needs to:

- choose an appropriate network model;
- specify a network topology (i.e., number of units and their connections);
- specify learning parameters.

Often the designer will have to pre-process the data. This pre-processing may be simple – for example, scaling each feature (i.e., variable) between 0 and 1 – or it may involve a more complicated statistical procedure. It should be stressed, however, that a long-term goal is to remove, more and more, the need for the designer to intervene and directly influence the solution since the great appeal of neural networks is their potential to devise their own solutions. In practice, much better progress is likely if one has good domain knowledge of the task to be solved and a good conceptual knowledge of neural network engineering.

The data that are available for training a network are usually split into two subsets: one for training and one for testing. It is really only during testing that the true performance of a neural network is revealed since it is possible to train a network successfully only to find it underperforms during testing. The testing is designed to assess the generalization capability of the network. Good generalization means that the network performs correctly on data that are similar to, but different from, the training data.

1.4 A simple training example

Let us look at a relatively simple problem and see how the simplest type of neural network can be used to solve that problem. The network will consist of just one input unit and one output unit.

Many of us at school have performed a physics experiment where we load a beam with weights and measure the deflection of the beam. We can then plot a graph of the deflection against the weight. The graph will show points that tend to follow a straight line. If we draw a line through the points using a method known as *least squares* we can then make a prediction of how much the beam will deflect with weights for which we have not measured the deflection. Many problems are modelled by fitting lines (or curves) to data. For instance, we may analyze production figures over the past few years to predict the number of washing machines a manufacturer will produce over the next two years. For data that follow a straight line we will obtain something like the scatter diagram shown in Figure 1.13. The data follow the trend of a straight line but do not fit exactly any straight line. This is to be expected since in the real world there will always be measurement errors.

Data

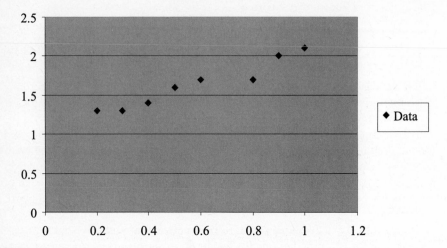

Figure 1.13 Data that follow the trend of a straight line but do not fit a straight line exactly because of measurement error.

The equation of a straight line is

$$y = mx + c$$

where y and x are variables (e.g., deflection and weight), m is the slope or gradient and c the intercept (i.e., where the line cuts the y-axis). We could fit a line by eye and measure the slope and intercept, but the method of least squares provides us with a way of calculating m and c. What do we mean by 'best'? We mean a line that minimizes the *sum of the squared errors* for all data points. The errors for a series of points are illustrated in Figure 1.14. The sum of the squared error is simply these errors squared and summed.

The method of least squares tells us that m is found from

$$m = \frac{n \sum x_i y_i - \sum x_i \sum y_i}{n \sum x_i^2 - (\sum x_i)^2} \tag{1.1}$$

and c from

$$c = \frac{\sum y_i - m \sum x_i}{n} \tag{1.2}$$

where x_i and y_i are the coordinate values for point i and n is the number of points. The summations are performed for all data points.

Error for this
point

Figure 1.14 Each point has an error which is its distance from the line.

1.4.1 How are the equations for m and c derived?

This subsection is optional but it might prove useful in helping to understand some of the theory introduced in Chapter 2.

Once a straight line is fitted to the data, a value for y can be estimated for any given value of x using the equation of the line. In reality, every estimated value of y is likely to have an error value. So, for an estimate of y we can write

$$y_i = mx_i + c + e_i \qquad (1.3)$$

where e_i is the error for point i. The sum of the squared errors, E, is

$$E = \sum_i e_i^2 \qquad (1.4)$$

Using equations (1.3) and (1.4) and rearranging, we obtain

$$E = \sum [y_i - (mx_i + c)]^2 \qquad (1.5)$$

We can see how the overall error varies with m and c by taking the partial derivatives of (1.5) with respect to m and c:

$$\frac{\partial E}{\partial m} = -2 \sum x_i[y_i - (mx_i + c)] \qquad (1.6)$$

$$\frac{\partial E}{\partial c} = -2 \sum [y_i - (mx_i + c)] \qquad (1.7)$$

If (1.6) and (1.7) are set equal to zero and the equations solved, we end up with (1.1) and (1.2).

The method of least squares gives an efficient way of finding the best straight line to fit a set of data. The method is easy to apply but its derivation requires some competence with basic mathematics. We can get a neural network to fit a line to a set of data. The network is simply presented with the sample data and left to learn.

A network with one input unit and one output unit was trained to place a straight line through the data in Figure 1.13. The network used a linear activation function. The task required the network to estimate m and c, and so m and c were the network's parameters (i.e., its weights) which were randomly

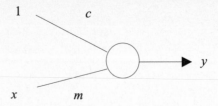

Figure 1.15 A single linear unit that can be trained to represent the line in Figure 1.16.

initialized before training between −0.3 and +0.3. The network model is shown in Figure 1.15. The training inputs were simply the x coordinate value for each point and the target value the y coordinate value. The weight c always has a value of 1 as its input (i.e., c multiplied by 1 is c: this weight is the bias). The network was trained using the delta rule with a learning rate of 0.1. Training was accomplished by presenting each point 10 000 times.

The estimates for m and c from the least-squares method and the network are as follows:

Parameter	Least squares	Network
m	1.0085	1.0284
c	1.0450	1.0360

and the line fitted by the network is shown in Figure 1.16.

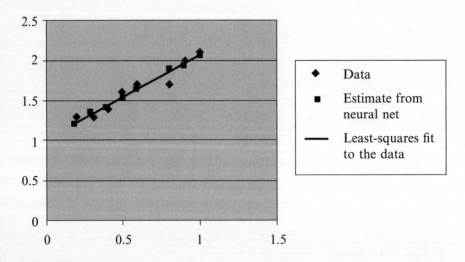

Figure 1.16 Data that have been fitted by a straight line using a neural network like that in Figure 1.15. The estimated line from the neural network is close to the least-squares fit.

It is not really surprising that the network gives comparable results to the least-squares equations since, as we shall see in Chapter 2, the delta learning rule is derived from the principle of minimizing the squared error. Our network has solved the given task of generating an output from a given input by fitting a line. In this case our network models a line, but large neural networks with nonlinear activation functions can fit very complex shapes around the training data and can therefore solve many types of very complicated task.

1.5 Summary

- A neural network is a collection of simple processing units which send signals to one another along weights.
- The way in which units are connected depends on the particular network model.
- A network unit has a rule for summing the signals coming in and a rule for calculating an output signal that is then sent to other network units. The rule for calculating the output is known as the activation function.
- A neural network can learn to perform a task and is not usually programmed in a more conventional sense. Learning is achieved by changing the values of the weights. During learning, a rule is used to decide by how much a weight should change.

1.6 Further reading

This book is designed to be an introduction to neural networks and to prepare the reader for more advanced texts. There will be numerous references to other reading material throughout this book. Some of the recommended reading material is very specific to some aspect of neural networks. The reader will also see references to the following texts which are highly recommended as more advanced books.

Fausett (1994) covers most of the topics included in the first two-thirds of our book but to a greater depth. Most neural network texts are very mathematical, and while Fausett's book is mathematical, the topics are presented with clear explanations and examples. (A new edition is to be published in 1998.)

Haykin (1994) is not for the mathematically shy. Network architectures are covered in depth. For most students the book is too advanced for a first course, but it is an excellent reference text if you wish to pursue your study of neural networks.

Rumelhart *et al.* (1986b) was largely responsible for the rekindled interest in neural networks following a very quiet period of research during the 1970s. Consequently, it has been widely cited in the literature on neural networks. Although the book is perhaps somewhat dated, it still holds many useful insights and is worth reading because of its place in the history of neural networks. Overall the book is readable; this author managed to code his first backpropagation network in C using the book as his only reference (*yes, the program worked!*).

1.7 Exercises

1 For the data given below, fit, by sketching, a number of lines through the data. Derive the equations of these lines by measuring the slope and intercept. For each line calculate the mean squared error given that the input is x and the output is

$$\text{output} = mx + c$$

x	Target output
0.30	1.60
0.35	1.40
0.40	1.40
0.50	1.60
0.60	1.70
0.80	2.00
0.95	1.70
1.10	2.10

2 For the data in Question 1, find the straight-line fit using the method of least squares.

3 For the data in Question 1, and given the start weights

$$\text{output} = 0.5x + 0.5$$

calculate the new line after one pass through the data using the Widrow–Hoff (delta) learning rule with a learning rate of 0.3. (*Note*: there will be a new line after each pattern has been presented.)

4 Our line-fitting neural network in Section 1.4 had a single input unit, and the aim was to find weights so that the value for y could be estimated when given x. As we shall see in Chapter 2, for many problems we wish to tell which side of a line (i.e., above or below) a data point falls. Rearrange the line derived in Question 2 into the form:

$$\text{input}(x, y) = mx - y + c$$

Calculate the input for all data points listed in Question 1 and for each point find an output value using the binary threshold function. How do you think the *input* calculation could be modelled by a neural network?

CHAPTER 2

Classifying patterns

Aims:	To describe the task of classification and to introduce neural networks capable of performing pattern classification.
Objectives:	You should be able to:

explain what a classification task is and what supervised learning is;
understand the basic concepts of how feedforward networks perform classification;
understand the feedforward backpropagation network to a level that would allow you to program one of these neural networks in a language of your choice;
describe the difference between a linear and nonlinear problem.

Prerequisites: Basic linear algebra to the level covered in Appendix A. For some sections, a basic understanding of differentiation is required but is not essential in order for the objectives listed above to be met. Chapter 1.

2.1 Applications

There are many applications that can be cast as classification problems. For example, if you are a bank manager and deciding whether or not someone is worthy of credit you may class that person as low-risk, medium-risk or high-risk. Optical character recognition succeeds by associating a scanned character with its correct class. Many variations on the image of the letter 'H', even for a specific font, exist – because the character might be smudged, for example – but all belong to the class 'H'. The recognition of a word from the acoustic signal emitted by a speaker is another example of classification.

When we know to which class each training instance belongs, supervised learning can be used. The task is for the network to learn how to map an input pattern to a target pattern that denotes the target class. For instance, the image of the letter 'H' might be passed to a neural network and we want to train the network so that an output unit that denotes 'H' will be switched on and all other units that denote other characters will be switched off. So the input pattern could be the grey-scale pixel values that make up the image and the target output pattern a vector with all elements set to zero apart from the element that denotes the output unit for 'H' which will be set to 1.

Most of this chapter is devoted to what is probably still the most widely used neural network model, the backpropagation network. This network has been used to solve a range of tasks from the recognition of objects from sonar signals to the modelling of dyslexia, which is a difficulty that some people have with recognizing words.

2.2 Fundamental ideas

This section will consider basic concepts before moving on to look at the backpropagation model in Section 2.4.

2.2.1 Decision function

To introduce the concept of how a neural network operates, a trivial task is presented and the most basic type of network is used to solve that task.

Figure 2.1 illustrates a classification task. The task is to provide rules to classify an aircraft as a bomber or fighter according to its maximum speed and maximum take-off weight. The rules could be given in symbol form:

IF weight > 0.80 AND speed < 0.55 THEN Bomber

IF weight < 0.90 AND speed > 0.25 THEN Fighter

The above rules use discrete limit values that effectively partition the space into rectangular regions. The partition provided by the rules will classify the aircraft depicted in the graph, but there will not be much room for error when an attempt is made to classify a new aircraft according to the rules. Also the rules

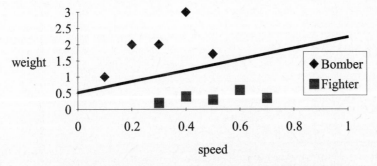

Figure 2.1 The separation of two classes using idealized data.

as they stand cannot provide any measure of how confident the classification of a new aircraft is.

An alternative approach to using rules is to derive a classification function by defining a line that separates the two classes. For a new aircraft we simply plot its position from knowledge of its maximum speed and maximum take-off weight and observe which side of the line the point lies. In the present scenario two features, speed and weight, are being considered for a small number of aircraft and therefore it is possible to view the data as a two-dimensional picture. However, when handling hundreds of aircraft with a large number of features (i.e., a multi-dimensional problem) it is no longer possible to view the classification task in a simple pictorial form.

The answer then is to use a decision function. The equation of the line that separates the two types of aircraft is

$$x_2 = 1.5x_1 + 0.5$$

where x_1 is speed and x_2 weight. This equation can be used to create a decision function:

$$f(x_1, x_2) = -x_2 + 1.5x_1 + 0.5$$

$$d = \begin{cases} \text{Fighter} & \text{if } f(x_1, x_2) \geq 0 \\ \text{Bomber} & \text{if } f(x_1, x_2) < 0 \end{cases}$$

For example, a fighter at (0.4, 0.5) will give

$$f(0.4, 0.5) = -0.5 + 1.5 \times 0.4 + 0.5 = 0.6$$

The decision function will classify the point correctly as a fighter.

The above decision function could be modelled by a neural network for possible implementation in hardware. Figure 2.2 is a network model of the decision function. The net input to the central unit is found by multiplying the input variables, x_1 and x_2, by their respective weighted connections and summing the results. The bias value indicated on the diagram is added into the

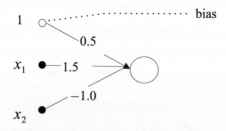

Figure 2.2 A simple neural network.

sum to calculate the total input to the unit. As noted in Chapter 1, this sum is expressed as

$$net_j = w_0 + \sum_{i=1}^{n} x_i w_{ij}$$

where net_j is the net total input, w_0 is the bias and is considered to be connected to a unit that always has an activation of 1, x_i is the activation for unit i and w_{ij} is the weight connecting from unit i to unit j. The unit in Figure 2.2 calculates an output value according to the threshold criterion

$$output = \begin{cases} 1 & \text{if total input} \geq 0 \\ 0 & \text{if total input} < 0 \end{cases}$$

An output value of 1 would indicate a fighter aircraft and an output of 0 would indicate a bomber aircraft.

The input to the network in Figure 2.2 is passed through the threshold function to produce the output of zero or one. This threshold function could be replaced by another function that produces an output ranging from zero to one. So, if the output is 0.9 we are fairly confident that the aircraft is a fighter, whereas with a value of 0.5 we are unsure as to its classification. In effect, a system is available that gives not only a classification but also a measure of the system's confidence in that classification.

EXAMPLE 2.1
    (a) Calculate the total net input to the unit in Figure 2.2 and the corresponding output assuming a threshold function and an input vector [0.7 2.5].
    (b) Calculate the output if the activation function is changed to the sigmoid function. The input vector is the same as in (a).
    (c) Calculate the net input for a network with the same architecture as that in Figure 2.2 but with weights [−0.2 0.03 1.2] and the same input vector as in (a).

SOLUTION 2.1
    (a) The order of elements in the vector indicates that $x_1 = 0.7$ and $x_2 = 2.5$. So the total input is

$$0.5 + (0.7 \times 1.5) + (2.5 \times -1) = -0.95$$

    The total input is negative and so the output is 0.
    (b) The activation for the sigmoid function is defined as

$$f(net_j) = \frac{1}{1 + \exp(-net_j)}$$

The net input is -0.95, and substituting into the sigmoid function gives an output of 0.28.

(c) The way in which the weight matrices are written in this book means that a *row* indexes the *connected-from* unit and a *column* the *connected-to* unit. The order of weights in the weight matrix means that the bias is -0.2, and since it is a bias the *connected-from* unit must have an activation of 1. With an input vector **x** and weight vector **w** the net input to a unit can be expressed as

$$net_j = \mathbf{xw}$$

provided that the input vector is written to include the bias activation. Adding the bias activation to the input vector, the net input is

$$net = [1 \quad 0.7 \quad 2.5] \begin{bmatrix} -0.2 \\ 0.03 \\ 1.2 \end{bmatrix}$$

$$= (1 \times -0.2) + (0.7 \times 0.03) + (2.5 \times 1.2)$$

$$= 2.82$$

EXAMPLE 2.2

Find the weights for a neural model similar to Figure 2.2 that represents the equation

$$2x_2 = -4x_1 + 8$$

SOLUTION 2.2

For any point that falls on the line, the weights will be defined such that

$$w_0 + x_1 w_1 + x_2 w_2 = 0$$

Rearranging gives

$$x_2 = -x_1 \frac{w_1}{w_2} - \frac{w_0}{w_2}$$

Equating terms gives

$$-\frac{w_1}{w_2} = -\frac{4}{2}, \qquad -\frac{w_0}{w_2} = \frac{8}{2}$$

So $w_0 = -8$, $w_1 = 4$ and $w_2 = 2$.

2.2.2 Adapting the weights

It should be obvious from Figure 2.1 that many straight lines can be drawn as the separating boundary and therefore many sets of weights exist to provide a solution. If t_j denotes the target or desired output from unit j and o_j the actual output, then the error E_p for a pattern p can be defined as

$$E_p = \frac{1}{2} \sum_j (t_j - o_j)^2 \tag{2.1}$$

and the overall error $E = \sum E_p$. The factor $\frac{1}{2}$ is included for ease of presentation in Section 2.2.3.

The activation for any unit is dependent on the net input to that unit and therefore is dependent on the weights impinging on that unit. Imagine a unit as in Figure 2.2 but with no bias. Such a unit can model any straight line that passes through the origin. For a linear unit and a single pattern, equation (2.1) can be written as

$$E = \frac{1}{2}(t - net)^2$$

because for a linear unit the output is the same as the input. Expanding gives

$$E = \frac{1}{2}[t^2 - 2t\,net + net^2]$$
$$= \frac{1}{2}[t^2 - 2t(x_1 w_1 + x_2 w_2) + x_1^2 w_1^2 + 2x_1 w_1 x_2 w_2 + x_2^2 w_2^2] \tag{2.2}$$

with $net = x_1 w_1 + x_2 w_2$. If we differentiate equation (2.2) with respect to w_1, we obtain

$$\frac{\partial E}{\partial w_1} = (-t + x_1 w_1 + x_2 w_2)x_1 \tag{2.3}$$

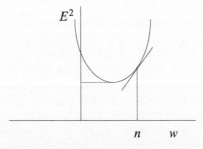

Figure 2.3 The line represents the derivative of the error with respect to a weight at time n.

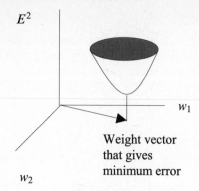

E^2

w_1

Weight vector
that gives
minimum error

w_2

Figure 2.4 The error can be plotted for different combinations of weights.

Equation 2.2 shows that if the squared error is plotted against w_1 the shape is parabolic as shown in Figure 2.3, and if equation (2.3) is set to 0 and solved the minimum point on the curve can be found.

Remember from Chapter 1 that, before training, the weights start at some random value and so the point representing the initial state of the network could be anywhere on the error surface but is very unlikely to be at its lowest point. So, during training, the network should seek to adapt its weights in a direction towards a lower overall error. In other words, the weights should be adjusted in the direction of steepest descent of the error surface. Figure 2.3 illustrates this idea for a single weight, where n denotes time or iteration. For two weights we obtain a bowl-shaped error surface like that shown in Figure 2.4.

2.2.3 Minimizing the squared error

A science experiment that many children will have performed at school is to plot the deflection of a beam against different loads and then to fit a best straight line by minimizing the sum of the squared differences between each point and the line. The same principle can be used to adapt weights, and one such rule for adapting weights is the Widrow–Hoff law or delta rule that we met in Chapter 1. This rule is

$$\Delta w_{ij} = \eta \delta_j x_i, \qquad \delta_j = (t_j - o_j) \tag{2.4}$$

where t_j is the target value of unit j, o_j is the actual output, x_i is the signal coming from unit i, η is the learning rate (by how much to adapt the weight) and Δw_{ij} is the amount by which to change the weight connecting unit i with j.

The rule is simple to derive for a linear unit with the output defined as

$$o_j = \sum_j x_i w_{ij}$$

The chain rule can be used to express the derivative of the error surface with respect to a weight as a product that reflects how the error changes with a unit's output and how the output changes with an impinging weight:

$$\frac{\partial E}{\partial w_{ij}} = \frac{\partial E}{\partial o_j} \frac{\partial o_j}{\partial w_{ij}} \qquad (2.5)$$

$$\frac{\partial E}{\partial o_j} = -\delta_j \qquad \text{from (2.1) and the definition of } \delta_j \text{ in (2.4)}$$

$$\frac{\partial o_j}{\partial w_{ij}} = x_i$$

and substituting back into (2.5) we obtain

$$-\frac{\partial E}{\partial w_{ij}} = \delta_j x_i$$

Taking into account that the weights need to change in a direction that is opposite to the direction of the gradient vector and that a learning rate is factored in, we end up with equation (2.4).

A modification to this method of adapting weights will be given in Section 2.4 to train networks with multiple layers of units, but before that we shall take a look at what advantage such a network offers over one with just a single layer of weights (i.e., a layer of input units and a layer of output units).

2.3 Linear and nonlinear problems

The network in Figure 2.2 has two input units for two features. The number of features denotes the dimension of the space from which all input patterns are drawn: so, for two features the space is two-dimensional, for three features the space is three-dimensional and for n features the space is n-dimensional. A simple network model consisting of three inputs and a single output unit will model a plane and for n inputs the model will be an n-dimensional hyperplane. For a classification task such as telling one aircraft type from another, if a line (for two dimensions) or a hyperplane for (n dimensions) can separate all patterns into their correct class then the problem is *linear*. If the problem requires multiple lines or hyperplanes to separate the patterns then the problem is *nonlinear*. A famous nonlinear example is the XOR problem introduced in Chapter 1. The XOR relation gives an output of 1 only when there is a single input set to 1, otherwise the output is 0. The XOR definition is given in Table 1.1. The XOR problem, then, is nonlinear and there are two options for solving it with a neural network: either use a network that will model two or

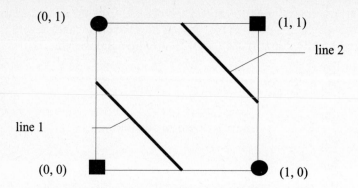

Figure 2.5 The XOR problem solved with two separating lines.

more lines to separate the data or change the inputs. The latter option can make the problem linear by augmenting the two input features with a third to make the inputs three-dimensional (the two classes will then reside on two different ends of a cube). We do not really consider this latter option to be a neural solution since augmenting with a third feature means we have intervened in helping to structure a solution and for many more complicated problems such intervention will not be possible. So, we prefer the network to sort out the nonlinearity. Therefore we shall concentrate on a solution that uses two lines to separate the data in their original two-dimensional form. The network then will require two units, both fed with two inputs, to represent the two lines and a third unit to combine the information from these two

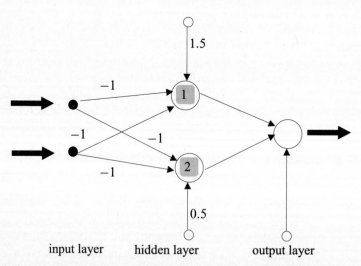

Figure 2.6 Neural net for modelling the XOR problem. The second layer of weights is shown later.

Table 2.1 *Response of hidden units for the network shown in Figure 2.6*

		Net input to hidden layer		Output from hidden layer	
x_1	x_2	Unit 1	Unit 2	Unit 1	Unit 2
1	1	−0.5	−1.5	0	0
1	0	0.5	−0.5	1	0
0	1	0.5	−0.5	1	0
0	0	1.5	0.5	1	1

lines. The XOR task with separating boundaries is illustrated in Figure 2.5. Figure 2.6 illustrates a neural network architecture that will model the two separating boundaries.

Let us examine what the first layer does to each input pattern. Units on the input layer will be indexed by i, units on the hidden layer by j and the output units by k. The network in Figure 2.6 has the units split into the three layers. The units in the first layer serve as input units to the network; remember that these units are different from units in subsequent layers because they have no transfer function – that is, the output from these units is the same as the input. The second layer of units is known as the *hidden* layer; the hidden units have only connections to other units and none to the external environment. The output layer serves to pass the network's response to the external world. Table 2.1 shows the net input and output (using a threshold function) of the units in the hidden layer in response to the inputs for the XOR problem.

The input patterns are transformed by the action of the first layer of weights and the hidden units. The second layer of weights connecting the hidden layer

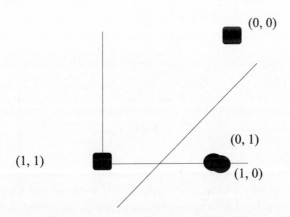

Figure 2.7 The effect of the first layer of weights has been to move the original point (0, 1) to (1, 0). Note that (0, 0) and (1, 1) have been transposed.

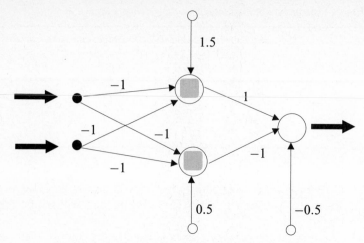

Figure 2.8 The complete network to solve the XOR problem.

to the output layer will also model a line since there will be two inputs and a bias passing values to the single output unit. If the output unit is to respond with the correct class for each input pattern, then the inputs to the second layer of weights must be linearly separable. We can check this by plotting the response of the hidden units as in Figure 2.7. Figure 2.8 shows the weights that define the separating line given in Figure 2.7.

To validate the network we shall check the network's response to each input pattern. The first layer of weights is

$$\begin{bmatrix} 1.5 & 0.5 \\ -1.0 & -1.0 \\ -1.0 & -1.0 \end{bmatrix}$$

where each weight is indexed by w_{ij}. So, the weight at at w_{10} is -1 which is the strength connecting unit 1 in the input layer to unit 1 in the hidden layer and corresponds to row 2, column 1 in the matrix because indexing starts from zero. Table 2.2 gives the complete response of the network in Figure 2.8 to the XOR inputs.

So far, then, we have manually derived a multi-layered neural network to solve the classic XOR problem, but what we are really interested in is a mechanism for the network to learn a solution for itself. Before we move on to look at a learning algorithm capable of learning a solution for itself, it is important to stress the role of the transfer or activation function found in each unit. The threshold function is a nonlinear activation function. An example of a linear function is the identity function, which simply states that the output is

Table 2.2 *Inputs and outputs for a 2-2-1 network*

Input vector p	First layer of weights Layer_1	Hidden layer response net input	output	Second layer of weights Layer_2	Output layer response input	output
[1| 1 1]	$\begin{bmatrix} 1.5 & 0.5 \\ -1.0 & -1.0 \\ -1.0 & -1.0 \end{bmatrix}$	[−0.5 −1.5]	[0 0]	$\begin{bmatrix} -0.5 \\ 1.0 \\ -1.0 \end{bmatrix}$	−0.5	0
[1| 1 0]	$\begin{bmatrix} 1.5 & 0.5 \\ -1.0 & -1.0 \\ -1.0 & -1.0 \end{bmatrix}$	[0.5 −0.5]	[1 0]	$\begin{bmatrix} -0.5 \\ 1.0 \\ -1.0 \end{bmatrix}$	0.5	1
[1| 0 1]	$\begin{bmatrix} 1.5 & 0.5 \\ -1.0 & -1.0 \\ -1.0 & -1.0 \end{bmatrix}$	[0.5 −0.5]	[1 0]	$\begin{bmatrix} -0.5 \\ 1.0 \\ -1.0 \end{bmatrix}$	0.5	1
[1| 0 0]	$\begin{bmatrix} 1.5 & 0.5 \\ -1.0 & -1.0 \\ -1.0 & -1.0 \end{bmatrix}$	[1.5 0.5]	[1 1]	$\begin{bmatrix} -0.5 \\ 1.0 \\ -1.0 \end{bmatrix}$	−0.5	0

the same as the input. The limitation of a network with linear units can be illustrated with the aid of Figure 2.9. The network has two input units, two hidden units and three output units. The weight matrices include the bias weights and are

$$\begin{bmatrix} 1.0 & -2.0 \\ 2.0 & 0.5 \\ -3.0 & 1.0 \end{bmatrix}$$

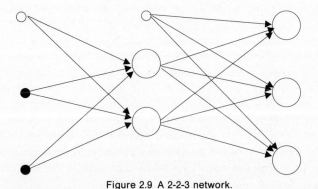

Figure 2.9 A 2-2-3 network.

for first layer of weights and

$$\begin{bmatrix} 2.0 & 1.0 & 3.0 \\ -1.0 & 5.0 & 4.0 \\ -3.0 & 1.0 & 2.0 \end{bmatrix}$$

for the second layer of weights.

For an input vector, [1.0 0.0 1.0], the input (and output because of the linear transfer function) to the hidden units is given by

$$[1.0 \quad 0.0 \quad 1.0] \begin{bmatrix} 1.0 & -2.0 \\ 2.0 & 0.5 \\ -3.0 & 1.0 \end{bmatrix} = [-2.0 \quad -1.0]$$

The input and output to the output layer is produced by augmenting the hidden units with the bias activation of 1.0 and multiplying by the second layer of weights:

$$[1.0 \quad -2.0 \quad -1.0] \begin{bmatrix} 2.0 & 1.0 & 3.0 \\ -1.0 & 5.0 & 4.0 \\ -3.0 & 1.0 & 2.0 \end{bmatrix} = [7.0 \quad -10.0 \quad -7.0]$$

Consider now the following multiplication:

$$[1.0 \quad 0.0 \quad 1.0] \begin{bmatrix} 5.0 & 3.0 & 3.0 \\ -3.5 & 10.5 & 9.0 \\ 2.0 & -13.0 & -10.0 \end{bmatrix} = [7.0 \quad -10.0 \quad -7.0]$$

This has given the same result as the previous one where two matrix multiplications were involved. The association law of matrix multiplication tells us that for linear activation functions a single layer of weights can be found that will achieve the same result as a network that has more than one layer of weights. In other words, a multi-layered network with linear activation functions will only be able to solve a problem that a single-layered network is capable of solving (i.e., a net with input and output units). Therefore nonlinear problems are ruled out. For multi-layered networks, then, a nonlinear activation function is required and for the algorithm that is to be presented, the function should be continuous, differentiable and monotonically increasing. A function satisfying the requirement is the logistic function (see Figure 1.10).

2.4 Backpropagation learning

For many years there was no rule available for updating the weights of a multi-layered network undergoing supervised training. In the 1970s Werbos developed a technique for adapting the weights but it was Rumelhart *et al.* (1986a) who gave a new lease of life to neural networks. The weight adaptation rule is known as *backpropagation*. For what follows, we assume a fully connected feedforward network, which means activation travels in a direction from the input layer to the output layer, and the units in one layer are connected to every other unit in the next layer up.

The backpropagation algorithm defines two sweeps of the network: first a forward sweep from the input layer to the output layer, and then a backward sweep from the output layer to the input layer. We have already seen that the forward sweep propagates input vectors through the network to provide outputs at the output layer. The backward sweep is similar to the forward sweep, except that error values are propagated back through the network to determine how the weights are to be changed during training. During the backward sweep, values pass along the weighted connections in the reverse direction to that which was taken during the forward sweep: for example, a unit in the hidden layer will send activation to every unit in the output layer during the forward sweep and so during the backward sweep a unit in the hidden layer will receive error signals from every unit in the output layer. This double sweep is illustrated in Figure 2.10.

During training each input pattern will have an associated target pattern. For example, for the input pattern of [1.0 0.0] in the XOR problem the network is

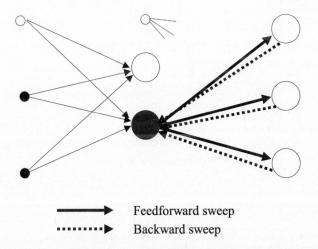

→ Feedforward sweep

┅┅┅► Backward sweep

Figure 2.10 The shaded hidden unit sends activation to each output unit, and so during the backward sweep this hidden unit will receive error signals from the output units.

required to output 1.0, and so 1.0 is the target value for this input pattern. The whole object of training is to find a set of network weights that provide a solution to the particular problem at hand. Before training commences the weights are set to small random values – for example, between −0.3 and 0.3. For reasons discussed earlier, a nonlinear activation function will be used. The sigmoid function will be the choice for the nonlinear function. The sigmoid can only produce values between 0 and 1 and because the function can never actually attain exactly 0 or 1, it is typical to use 0.1 instead of 0 and 0.9 instead of 1.0. The choice, however, of 0.1 and 0.9 is not too critical since a network is usually considered to have learnt a task once all outputs fall within a specified tolerance with respect to their target values. For example, if the target output is 1.0 and the tolerance is 0.1, then any actual output between 0.9 and 1.0 will be within the specified tolerance. The procedure for backpropagation training is as follows:

```
for each input vector associate a target output vector
while not STOP
  STOP = TRUE
    for each input vector
      perform a forward sweep to find the actual output
      obtain an error vector by comparing the actual and target output
      if the actual output is not within tolerance set STOP = FALSE
      perform a backward sweep of the error vector
      use the backward sweep to determine weight changes
      update weights
```

In summary, a pattern is presented to the network and an error vector is calculated to determine how the weights should change; the process is then repeated for each pattern. An epoch is a complete cycle through each pattern (i.e., each pattern has been presented to the network). The patterns are continually presented to the network, epoch after epoch, until during one epoch all actual outputs for each pattern are within tolerance.

2.4.1 Some theory

Backpropagation uses a generalization of the delta rule. This subsection is based on the presentation given by Rumelhart et $al.$ (1986a). For a more in-depth presentation, the interested reader is referred to Rumelhart et $al.$ (1986a) or Werbos (1990).

We can express the error derivative as

$$\frac{\partial E}{\partial w_{ij}} = \frac{\partial E}{\partial o_j} \frac{\partial o_j}{\partial net_j} \frac{\partial net_j}{\partial w_{ij}} \tag{2.6}$$

We define δ_j by

$$\delta_j = -\frac{\partial E}{\partial net_j} \tag{2.7}$$

The original delta rule in Section 2.2.3 gave the definition as $\delta_j = -\partial E/\partial o_j$. The definitions are consistent though, since the original delta rule is for linear units where the output is the same as the input. Equation (2.7) can be rewritten as

$$\delta_j = -\frac{\partial E}{\partial o_j}\frac{\partial o_j}{\partial net_j}$$

Since $E_p = \frac{1}{2}\sum_j (t_j - o_j)^2$, we have

$$\frac{\partial E}{\partial o_j} = -(t_j - o_j)$$

For activation function f (typically the logistic function) the output is

$$o_j = f(net_j)$$

and so the derivative f' is given by

$$\frac{\partial o_j}{\partial net_j} = f'(net_j)$$

So

$$\delta_j = (t_j - o_j)f'(net_j)$$

The standard summation of products is used to find the net total input

$$net_j = \sum_{i=0} x_i w_{ij}$$

and so

$$\frac{\partial net_j}{\partial w_{ij}} = x_i$$

So taking the product of each derivative and substituting back into (2.6) gives

$$\frac{\partial E}{\partial w_{ij}} = -(t_j - o_j)f'(net_j)x_i$$

Noting that the weight change should be in a direction opposite to the derivative of the error surface and applying a learning rate η, the weight change for a unit is

$$\Delta w_{ij} = \eta \delta_j x_i$$

The error δ_j given above is applicable to an output unit, but the error for a hidden unit is not directly related to the target output. However, a hidden unit can be adapted in proportion to its assumed contribution to the error in the next layer up (i.e., the output layer for a net with a single hidden layer). For a network with a single hidden layer, by propagating error signals back through the network, the error from each output unit will make a contribution to the error of each hidden unit. That contribution to a hidden unit will depend on the size of the error for an output unit and the strength of the weight that connects both units. In other words, an output unit with a high error makes a strong contribution to the error of any hidden unit that is connected by a weight with a high strength. For a hidden unit the error is given by

$$\delta_j = f'(net_j) \sum_k \delta_k w_{kj}$$

where k indexes the layer sending back the error which will be the output layer for a network with a single hidden layer.

A suitable activation function is the logistic function

$$f(net_j) = \frac{1}{1 + \exp(-net_j)}$$

The derivative of this activation function is

$$f'(net_j) = \frac{\exp(-net_j)}{(1 + \exp(-net_j))^2}$$

$$= \frac{1}{1 + \exp(-net_j)} \left(1 - \frac{1}{1 + \exp(-net_j)} \right)$$

$$= f(net_j)[1 - f(net_j)]$$

2.4.2 The backpropagation algorithm

The first stage is to initialize the weights to small random values – for example, between -0.3 and $+0.3$. The training is supervised by having a target pattern associated with an input pattern. Training continues until the change in the absolute value of the averaged squared error falls to within some tolerance between one epoch and the next epoch. For example, a tolerance of 0.01 means that the averaged squared error must not change by more than ± 0.01 between successive epochs. If a network meets the tolerance during training it is said to have *converged*. An alternative way to judge the end of training is to insist that each target ouput for each training pattern be within some specified tolerance.

To reduce the likelihood of the weight changes oscillating, a momentum term, α, is introduced that adds in a proportion of the previous weight change:

$$\Delta w_{ij}(n+1) = \eta(\delta_j o_i) + \alpha \Delta w_{ij}(n)$$

So the weight change for pattern $n+1$ is dependent on the weight change for pattern n. The backpropagation algorithm is summarized in Figure 2.11.

We shall look at some small example calculations next, but if you still find the algorithm somewhat intimidating or unclear there is a full example of the calculations given for a network in Section 2.7. This network has two hidden layers and you might find it useful to trace through the calculations.

EXAMPLE 2.3

Perform a complete forward and backward sweep of a feedforward network using the backpropagation algorithm for an input pattern of [0.1 0.9] with a target output of 0.9 and a 2-2-1 architecture (i.e., two input, two hidden and one output unit) with weights

$$\begin{bmatrix} 0.1 & 0.1 \\ -0.2 & -0.1 \\ 0.1 & 0.3 \end{bmatrix}$$

for the first layer and

$$\begin{bmatrix} 0.2 \\ 0.2 \\ 0.3 \end{bmatrix}$$

for second layer.

SOLUTION 2.3

The output for the input units is simply the input pattern. The first row of either weight matrix defines the bias terms for each layer which, remember, are attached to a unit with an activation of 1. The units are numbered as $\{0, 1, 2\}$ for the input layer, $\{3, 4, 5\}$ for the hidden layer and

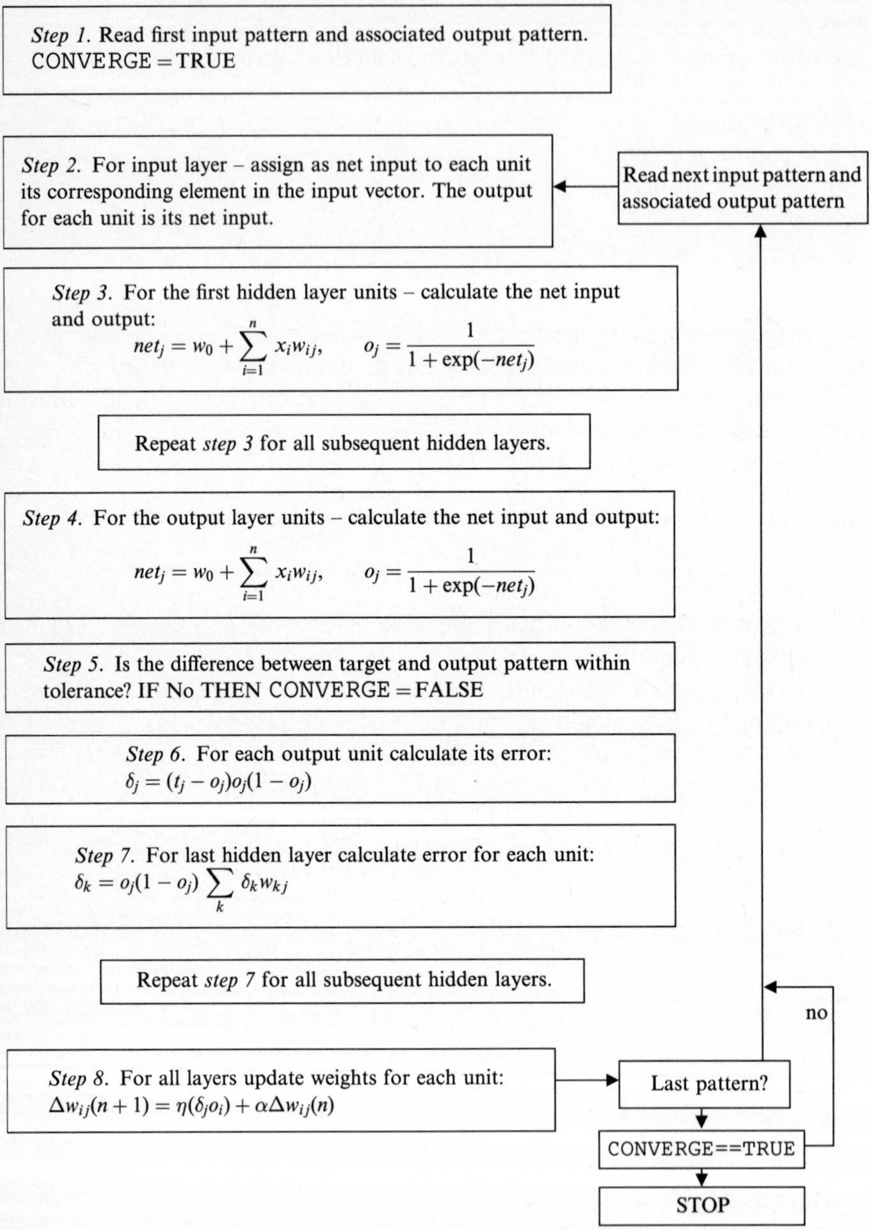

Step 1. Read first input pattern and associated output pattern.
CONVERGE = TRUE

Step 2. For input layer – assign as net input to each unit its corresponding element in the input vector. The output for each unit is its net input.

Read next input pattern and associated output pattern

Step 3. For the first hidden layer units – calculate the net input and output:
$$net_j = w_0 + \sum_{i=1}^{n} x_i w_{ij}, \qquad o_j = \frac{1}{1 + \exp(-net_j)}$$

Repeat *step 3* for all subsequent hidden layers.

Step 4. For the output layer units – calculate the net input and output:
$$net_j = w_0 + \sum_{i=1}^{n} x_i w_{ij}, \qquad o_j = \frac{1}{1 + \exp(-net_j)}$$

Step 5. Is the difference between target and output pattern within tolerance? IF No THEN CONVERGE = FALSE

Step 6. For each output unit calculate its error:
$$\delta_j = (t_j - o_j)o_j(1 - o_j)$$

Step 7. For last hidden layer calculate error for each unit:
$$\delta_k = o_j(1 - o_j) \sum_{k} \delta_k w_{kj}$$

Repeat *step 7* for all subsequent hidden layers.

no

Step 8. For all layers update weights for each unit:
$$\Delta w_{ij}(n + 1) = \eta(\delta_j o_i) + \alpha \Delta w_{ij}(n)$$

Last pattern?

CONVERGE==TRUE

STOP

Figure 2.11 The backpropagation algorithm. The index *k* refers to a previous layer in the reverse sense (i.e., when moving back through the net). The notation is further explained in Appendix A.

{6} for the output layer, with units 0 and 3 being the bias units for the input and hidden layer, respectively.

$$net_4 = (1.0 \times 0.1) + (0.1 \times -0.2) + (0.9 \times 0.1)$$

$$= 0.170$$

$$o_4 = \frac{1}{1 + \exp(-0.17)}$$

$$= 0.542$$

$$net_5 = (1.0 \times 0.1) + (0.1 \times -0.1) + (0.9 \times 0.3)$$

$$= 0.360$$

$$o_5 = \frac{1}{1 + \exp(-0.36)}$$

$$= 0.589$$

Similarly, from the hidden to output layer:

$$net_6 = (1.0 \times 0.2) + (0.542 \times 0.2) + (0.589 \times 0.3)$$
$$= 0.485$$
$$o_6 = 0.619$$

The error for the output node is:

$$\delta_6 = (0.9 - 0.619) \times 0.619 \times (1 - 0.619)$$
$$= 0.066$$

The error for the hidden nodes is:

$$\delta_5 = 0.589 \times (1.0 - 0.589) \times (0.066 \times 0.3)$$
$$= 0.005$$
$$\delta_4 = 0.542 \times (1.0 - 0.542) \times (0.066 \times 0.2)$$
$$= 0.003$$

Note that the hidden unit errors are used to update the first layer of weights. There is no error calculated for the bias unit as no weights from the first layer connect to the hidden bias.

The rate of learning for this example is taken as 0.25. There is no need to give a momentum term for this first pattern since there are no previous weight changes.

$$\Delta w_{5,6} = 0.25 \times 0.066 \times 0.589$$
$$= 0.01$$

The new weight is:

$$0.3 + 0.01 = 0.31$$
$$\Delta w_{4,6} = 0.25 \times 0.066 \times 0.542$$
$$= 0.009$$

Then:

$$0.2 + 0.009 = 0.209$$
$$\Delta w_{3,6} = 0.25 \times 0.066 \times 1.0$$
$$= 0.017$$

Finally:

$$0.2 + 0.017 = 0.217$$

The calculation of the new weights for the first layer is left as an exercise.

EXAMPLE 2.4

Figure 2.12 shows the hidden and output layers of a feedforward network. Calculate the error for hidden unit U given that its activation for the pattern being processed is currently 0.64.

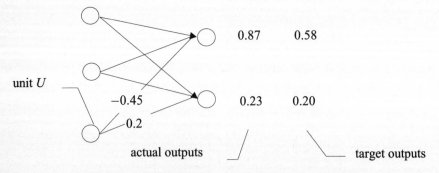

Figure 2.12 A simple network – the input layer is not shown.

SOLUTION 2.4

The errors for the output units are calculated first:

$$\delta_{\text{output}\_1} = (0.58 - 0.87) \times 0.87 \times (1 - 0.87)$$
$$= -0.033$$
$$\delta_{\text{output}\_2} = (0.20 - 0.23) \times 0.23 \times (1 - 0.23)$$
$$= -0.005$$

The errors are now propagated back to unit U:

$$\delta_U = 0.64 \times (1 - 0.64) \times [(-0.033 \times -0.45) + (-0.005 \times 0.20)]$$
$$= 0.003$$

2.4.3 Some practical considerations

A number of practical points to consider when using backpropagation networks are given in this subsection, but the reader should also refer to Section 6.4 for a more detailed discussion. The successful application of a neural network usually demands much experimentation. There are a number of parameters to be set that can affect how easy it is to find a solution. For feedforward networks, the number of hidden units and the number of layers can be varied. Certainly, the training data are an important factor and a good deal of attention must be paid to the test data so that we can be sure the network will generalize correctly on data with which it has not been trained. Indeed, it is possible to train a network on data with complete success only to find the network fails when processing new data. For any new style of application there is no prescribed way of finding a solution. Sometimes the problem appears intractable, but failure to find a solution does not mean that the application is not amenable to a neural solution. Although applying neural networks involves a 'try and see' approach, the requirement for knowledge of the application domain and knowledge of neural networks should not be underestimated.

Theory tells us that a network with a single hidden layer can represent any continuous mapping of the form

$$y = f(x)$$

Since this form of mapping is the basis for many real-world problems, is there a need for more than one hidden layer? Well, a network with two hidden layers can sometimes be easier to train and a variant of the feedforward net known as an autoassociator may use multiple hidden layers to perform data compression (see Chapter 4).

The learning algorithm as it has been presented uses pattern updating of the weights, which simply means that the weights are updated after each pattern presentation. It can sometimes prove quicker to train a network using batch updating, where the error for a unit is accumulated for one epoch before adapting the unit's weights. However, it can be beneficial to randomize the order of presentation for each training pattern between epochs in which case pattern updating is required. Usually, it is best to experiment with different approaches.

Generalization

If a network can produce the correct output for the majority of input patterns in the test data set, the network is said to *generalize* well. It is assumed that the test data set was not used during training.

If a network is trained well to produce a smooth nonlinear mapping, it should be able to interpolate to new patterns that are similar to but not exactly the same as those patterns used for training. A non-smooth mapping results when the network is overtrained. In this situation the network will work more like a memory, looking up an output for a certain input from the training set.

Good generalization is dependent on the training set and network architecture. The training data set must be representative of the problem being tackled, but the number of hidden units is also an important factor. If there are more hidden units than is required to learn the input–output relationship, there will be more weights than necessary and overfitting of the data can result if training goes on for too long. Sometimes a subset of the training data is used to act as an interim test when experimenting with different network architectures and lengths of training time. The main test data set is still reserved for the final test of generalization.

The application of neural networks is an experimental approach to engineering. General guidelines sometimes exist for network design. Haykin (1994) uses a result derived by Baum and Haussler (1989) to give a guideline as to the size of the training data set. The guideline states that

$$N > \frac{W}{\varepsilon}$$

where N is the number of training patterns, W is the number of network weights and ε is the proportion of allowed errors in testing. So, for a 10% error the number of training patterns should be 10 times the number of weights.

2.5 Applying the backpropagation network

In this chapter we have been looking at a class of problems that can be cast as mapping some input pattern into one of a number of classes. For the XOR problem the number of classes is two and a single output unit with two states will suffice (i.e., the state 'less than 0.1' is OFF while 'greater than 0.9' is ON).

A common approach is to assign an output unit for each class. If the input pattern is drawn, say, from class C_k then output unit U_k should be switched on and all others switched off.

2.5.1 Classifying numerals

The task is to classify the digits 0 to 9. There are 10 classes and so each target vector could be a 1-in-10 vector. For example, the target for 2 could be [0 0 1 0 0 0 0 0 0 0], which indicates that the third output unit should be on and all others off.

In the case study presented here, the target values are represented by 1-in-9 vectors for the numerals 1 to 9, with zero being represented by all bits being switched off. For example, if the network believes it is looking at the number 2 then the second output unit will be 1, with all others set to 0. The numerals to be learnt are shown in Figure 2.13. Each numeral is represented by a 9×7 grid, with a grey pixel being 0 and a black pixel being 1.

A 63-6-9 network architecture is chosen: 9×7 input units (one for each pixel), six hidden units and nine output units for the target vectors. The pixels are mapped into the input layer as shown in Figure 2.14.

The network was trained for 600 epochs using a learning rate of 0.3 and a momentum of 0.7. An output unit was considered to be on if its activation was greater than 0.9 and off if its activation was less than 0.1.

The network trained successfully. It was then tested on the data in Figure 2.15. Each of the numbers has one or more bits missing. All the test numbers were correctly identified, apart from 8. The sixth output unit had an activation of 0.53 and the eighth unit an activation of 0.41. The net was confused as to whether the eighth pattern was the numeral 8 or 6, and was not confident of either possibility.

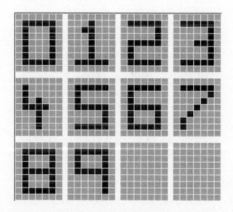

Figure 2.13 Training data.

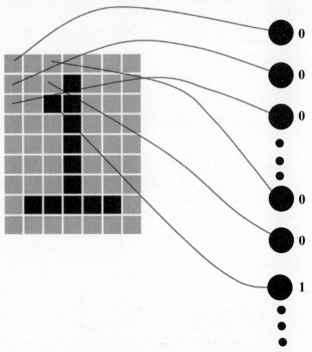

Figure 2.14 The grid is mapped to the input layer by treating it as a long string of bits that are set to 0 or 1. The bits are mapped by starting at the top left-hand corner, working down the grid for the first column and then repeating for each other column.

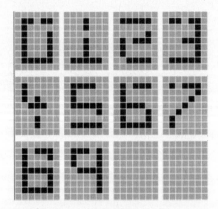

Figure 2.15 Noisy test data.

2.5.2 Classifying characters

This task is similar to the previous one of identifying numerals. The task is to train a feedforward network to recognize the characters A, B, C, D. The training characters are drawn from three different fonts. A fourth type of font is used to test the network. The characters are shown in Figure 2.16. They were drawn on 16×16 pixel grids, and so there are 256 input units. There are four output units, one for each class.

The network will train successfully and generalize correctly with a variety of architectures. It trains easily using a single hidden layer of eight units and performs correctly on the test set. The network nearly always succeeds in learning the training data. However, it fails on the test set just as often as it succeeds following different training sessions. The failure is usually with one single test character that the network classifies incorrectly. The network has plenty of resources to perform the task with eight or fewer hidden units. As expected, generalization degrades with a high number of hidden units, but occasionally it will succeed even with 100 or more hidden units.

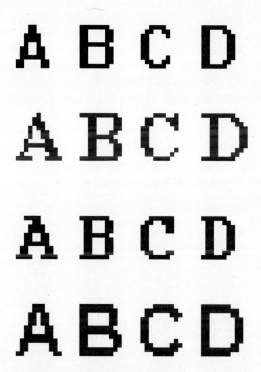

Figure 2.16. The top three sets of characters form the training set and the bottom row of characters the test set.

2.5.3 Predicting the weather

To get a neural network to predict the weather with any reliability would most likely require an enormous research program. It is a large problem and scientists have spent many years developing sophisticated computer programs to assist with forecasts. However, by way of an exercise we can discuss how we might approach the development of a system to predict tomorrow's weather from today's weather. We might call it the 'naïve forecaster'.

Table 2.3 presents some data gathered from a weather station in the UK on five features for 10 days. We could attempt to perform our prediction task by presenting the network with the weather for day 1 and use day 2 as the target output. The second training pattern would be day 2 with day 3 as the target and so on. Our network would have five input units and five output units. We might start with a large number of hidden units (say 30) and gradually attempt to reduce the number. We would, of course, require far more data than 10 days' worth. Given a large data set, we would extract both training and test data sets. The data would also need to be pre-processed so that all the numbers fell within the range of the activation units (i.e., 0.1 to 0.9 for the sigmoid function). The data in their raw form without pre-processing are unsuitable. Not only does the range of the data fall outside of the range of the activation function; there is also a large variance in the features. For instance, pressure has values in the order of 1000 whereas for rain the values are less than 10. We do not want to bias the network towards pressure being more important than rainfall and so the data must be pre-processed. The pre-processing of data is discussed in Chapter 6.

Although we might not have much confidence in our ability to develop a weather forecasting system using such a simple approach as that given above, there is no harm in trying. We might discover that it is possible to produce a reasonably good short-term forecast (i.e., for tomorrow). Indeed, there are

Table 2.3 *Sample of weather data*

Day	Temperature (°C)		Rain (mm)	Pressure (mb)	Sun (hours)
	min.	max.			
01	−1	4.8	0.7	1011	3.8
02	−1	2.8	0	1024	5.4
03	−5.3	3.6	0	1032	4.8
04	−5	6.6	2.8	1026.5	0
05	3.5	4.7	3	1019.5	0
06	1.5	7.9	0	1018.5	5.2
07	−1.4	9.5	0.2	1034.5	0
08	0.8	10.4	1.4	1028.5	0.2
09	1.8	10.4	0.4	1028.5	0
10	4	12	2	1020.5	0

people attempting such a task. Knowledge of weather forecasting would help us structure the problem and identify the most useful data. For instance, it would seem reasonable to assume that a better forecast would be obtained from monitoring how the data are changing throughout the day rather than using a simple summary of total rainfall and highest temperature, etc.

The weather forecasting task is typical of a neural network task. There is information that we believe is representative of the problem being tackled but the difficult part is deciding how to use the data and how to choose an appropriate neural network architecture to tackle the problem. Making a good start is down to experience and some inspired ideas of what might work. Through experimenting with the problem you get to understand more about the data and more ideas develop as to how the problem should be tackled.

2.6 Radial basis function networks

In this section we consider another type of network model that can be used for pattern classification, the radial basis function network.

A radial basis function network in its simplest form is a three-layered network with the usual input layer to distribute a pattern to the first layer of weights, a hidden layer and an output layer. The input layer to hidden layer mapping is nonlinear and the hidden layer to output layer mapping is linear. Usually (but not always), the number of hidden units exceeds the number of input units. The idea is that if a nonlinear problem is cast into a high-dimensional space in a nonlinear manner then it is more likely to be linearly separable.

The mapping of the first layer works as follows. For each hidden unit there is a function φ. Each of these functions takes the net input and produces an activation value as output. The collective activations of all the hidden units define the vector to which the input vector has been mapped:

$$\varphi(\mathbf{x}) = [\varphi(x_1), \varphi(x_2), \dots, \varphi(x_M)]$$

where M is the number of hidden units and $\mathbf{x}$ is the input vector.

The weights connecting to a hidden unit define the centre of the radial basis function for that hidden unit. The input to a unit is then taken to be the Euclidean norm:

$$net_j = \|\mathbf{x} - \mathbf{w}_j\|$$

$$= \left[\sum_{i=1}^{n} (x_i - w_{ij})^2 \right]^{1/2}$$

where n is the number of input units.

Various nonlinear hidden unit activation functions are used. Broomhead and Lowe (1988) used a Gaussian form, $\varphi(r) \approx \exp[-r^2]$, or multiquadric form, $\varphi(r) \approx \sqrt{c^2 + r^2}$.

EXAMPLE 2.5

A 2-2-1 radial basis function network is used to solve the XOR problem. The first layer of weights is given by

$$\begin{bmatrix} 1 & 0 \\ 1 & 0 \end{bmatrix}$$

Calculate the activations for the hidden units, for each XOR pattern, using an activation function of the form $\varphi(net) = \exp[-net^2]$, where net is the Euclidean norm.

SOLUTION 2.5

For pattern $(0, 1)$ and the first hidden unit,

$$\varphi_1 = \exp[-[(0 - 1)^2 + (1 - 1)^2]] = \exp[-1] = 0.368$$

For pattern $(0, 1)$ and the second hidden unit,

$$\varphi_2 = \exp[-[(0 - 0)^2 + (1 - 0)^2]] = \exp[-1] = 0.368$$

The complete set of activations is as follows:

Input	φ_1	φ_2
$(0, 1)$	0.368	0.368
$(1, 0)$	0.368	0.368
$(0, 0)$	0.135	1
$(1, 1)$	1	0.135

If the hidden activations are plotted it will be seen that the patterns are now linearly separable.

There are several techniques for determining the weights. The first layer of weights could be fixed before training by randomly selecting each hidden function centre from the training data. The first layer of weights is typically found using an unsupervised technique (see Chapter 3). Once the first layer of weights has been found the second layer of weights can sometimes be determined directly or, failing that, a linear supervised learning algorithm can be used.

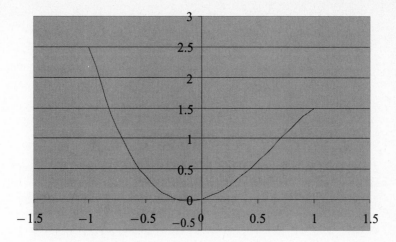

Figure 2.17 The plot of $f(x) = 0.5x + 2x^2 - x^3$.

Both radial basis function networks and multi-layered backpropagation networks can be made to solve the same problem. These networks are very generalized computing devices and can be applied to a range of tasks. We shall look at one more example of using a radial basis function network for approximating a function. The functions is

$$f(x) = 0.5x + 2x^2 - x^3$$

and is plotted in Figure 2.17.

The curve will be approximated using a weighted sum of Gaussian functions of the form

$$net_j = \exp\left[-\frac{1}{2\sigma}(c - x)^2 \right]$$

where c is the function centre. An example Gaussian curve centred at zero is shown in Figure 2.18. The constant σ controls the width of the bell-shaped curve.

The number of basis functions was chosen arbitrarily. Nine functions were chosen with centres $\{-0.8, -0.6, -0.4, -0.2, 0, 0.2, 0.4, 0.6, 0.8\}$. The width was 0.5. The curve is approximated using a weighted sum of the functions. The Gaussian functions represent the hidden layer of the network and so there are nine units in the hidden layer. The first layer of weights from the single input unit is simply the set of function centres. The second layer of weights is found

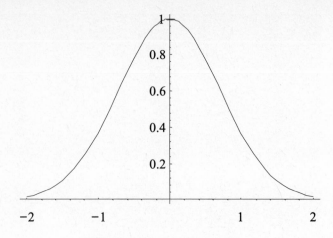

Figure 2.18 The Gaussian function.

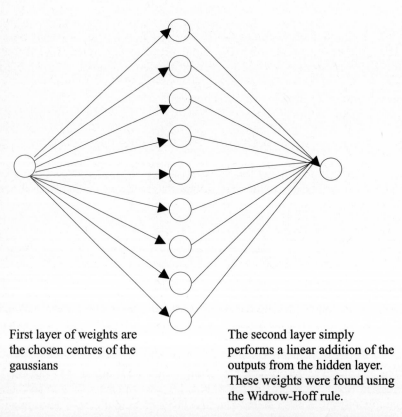

First layer of weights are the chosen centres of the gaussians

The second layer simply performs a linear addition of the outputs from the hidden layer. These weights were found using the Widrow-Hoff rule.

Figure 2.19 Radial basis function network trained to represent the curve in Figure 2.17.

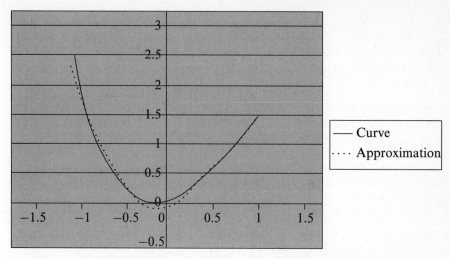

Figure 2.20 Curve approximated using the radial basis function network in Figure 2.19.

using the Widrow–Hoff learning rule presented in Chapter 1: for an output of o and a target output t, the error, δ, is given by

$$\delta = t - o$$

The total signal coming into the output unit is *net*. The Widrow–Hoff learning law (i.e., basic delta rule) states that the adjustment to be made, Δw, is

$$\Delta w = \eta \delta \, net$$

The network architecture is shown in Figure 2.19. The learning rate was set at 0.1. To find the second layer of weights, 21 training patterns were generated by passing a number (in the range -1 to $+1$) through the first layer of weights. The activations of the hidden layer then give a vector with nine elements for each training point. These 21 vectors form the training patterns for the linear network and the associated target outputs are derived from the original function of the curve. The approximation generated by the network is shown plotted against the original curve in Figure 2.20.

In practice, we would determine the network's weights and test its performance; we might then adjust the first layer of weights followed by the second layer in an attempt to improve performance. We follow a process of experimenting with network parameters until the performance is acceptable.

2.7 Summary

This chapter has looked at supervised learning, where the object is to map an input pattern to a target pattern. For supervised learning it is necessary to have:

- data that have a known classification;
- sufficient data to represent all aspects of the problem being solved;
- sufficient data to allow for testing.

The test data set and the training data set should be disjoint (so that test data are not used during training). The knowledge of the solved task resides in the network's weights.

The backpropagation algorithm is in wide use:

- It learns by adapting its weights using the generalized delta rule which attempts to minimize the squared error between what is the desired network output and the actual network output.
- During learning it continually cycles through the data until the error is at a low enough value for the task to be considered solved. Even when the squared error is low, it is important to check that individual training patterns are all correctly classified.
- Following training, the network's weights are fixed and the network can then be used to classify an unknown pattern.
- A single hidden layer of units is theoretically sufficient for a task to be learned but in practice more than one hidden layer could give better performance.
- Backpropagation networks can take a long time to train.
- Generalization is a measure of how well the network performs on data not seen during training. The number of hidden units and the length of training can have a significant effect on generalization.

A radial basis function network is another network used for classification (or general function fitting):

- It requires sufficient data that represent all aspects of the problem being solved.
- It requires sufficient data to allow testing. The test data set and the training data set should be disjoint (i.e., test data are not used during training).
- It solves a nonlinear problem by casting the input patterns into a higher-dimensional space in a nonlinear way.
- The choice of activation function for the hidden units must be made prior to learning. A form of Gaussian function is typical.
- The centres of the Gaussian functions define the first layer of weights. These can be determined using a clustering technique (see Chapter 3).

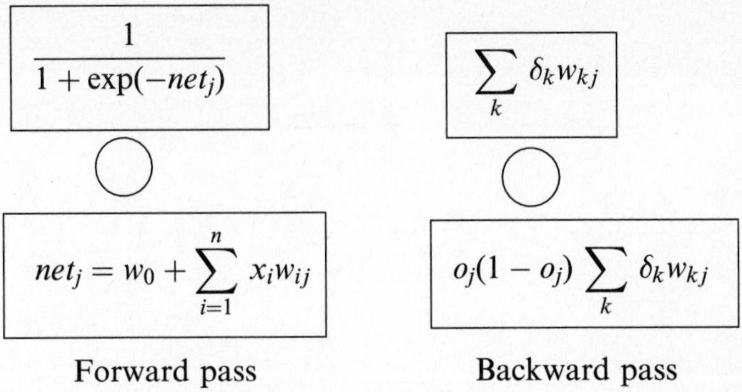

$$\boxed{\frac{1}{1 + \exp(-net_j)}}$$

$$\boxed{\sum_k \delta_k w_{kj}}$$

◯ ◯

$$\boxed{net_j = w_0 + \sum_{i=1}^n x_i w_{ij}}$$

$$\boxed{o_j(1 - o_j) \sum_k \delta_k w_{kj}}$$

Forward pass   Backward pass

Figure 2.21 The numbers before and after the units in Figure 2.22 correspond to the boxed calculations.

- The second layer of the network's weights can be determined using a linear supervised learning rule.

The main emphasis of this chapter has been on the backpropagation network, and so we shall present one more example in diagram form of a complete forward and backward pass. The input is $(0.1, 0.9)$, the learning rate is 0.8 and the momentum 0. The network is a 2-2-2-1 architecture and the weights are:

$$\begin{bmatrix} 2 & 2 \\ -2 & 3 \\ -2 & 3 \end{bmatrix} \begin{bmatrix} 3 & -2 \\ -2 & 2 \\ -4 & 2 \end{bmatrix} \begin{bmatrix} -2 \\ 3 \\ 1 \end{bmatrix}$$

where each matrix represents a layer of weights. Figure 2.22 shows the forward sweep through the network with the total input to a unit and the total output given. The backward sweep of errors shows the weighted error received by a unit and the total error as indicated in Figure 2.21. Figure 2.23 shows the new weights.

2.8 Further reading

The original exposition of the backpropagation by Rumelhart *et al.* (1986a) is still worth studying. The later paper by Werbos (1990) also describes the theory behind backpropagation and a variation with recurrent connections (see Chapter 5). For the radial basis function networks, the paper by Broomhead and Lowe (1988) should be studied, and Haykin (1994) provides a detailed introduction.

There are many variations of the backpropagation algorithm to speed up training and to help the network avoid the problem of local minima which can

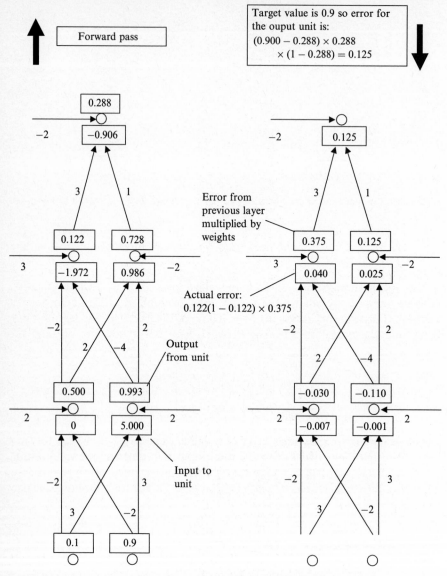

Figure 2.22 Example of a forward pass and a backward pass through a 2-2-2-1 feedforward network. Inputs, outputs and errors are shown in boxes (see Figure 2.21).

result in the network failing to learn. Some of these points are covered further in Chapter 6, but the keen reader is referred once again to Haykin (1994) and to Masters (1995) who provides a practical insight to solving these issues using the C++ language.

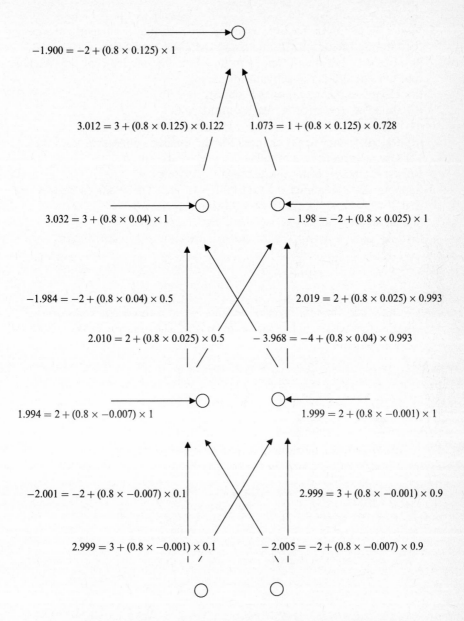

$-1.900 = -2 + (0.8 \times 0.125) \times 1$

$3.012 = 3 + (0.8 \times 0.125) \times 0.122$ $1.073 = 1 + (0.8 \times 0.125) \times 0.728$

$3.032 = 3 + (0.8 \times 0.04) \times 1$ $-1.98 = -2 + (0.8 \times 0.025) \times 1$

$-1.984 = -2 + (0.8 \times 0.04) \times 0.5$ $2.019 = 2 + (0.8 \times 0.025) \times 0.993$

$2.010 = 2 + (0.8 \times 0.025) \times 0.5$ $-3.968 = -4 + (0.8 \times 0.04) \times 0.993$

$1.994 = 2 + (0.8 \times -0.007) \times 1$ $1.999 = 2 + (0.8 \times -0.001) \times 1$

$-2.001 = -2 + (0.8 \times -0.007) \times 0.1$ $2.999 = 3 + (0.8 \times -0.001) \times 0.9$

$2.999 = 3 + (0.8 \times -0.001) \times 0.1$ $-2.005 = -2 + (0.8 \times -0.007) \times 0.9$

Figure 2.23 New weights calculated following the errors derived in Figure 2.22.

2.9 Exercises

1 Figure 2.24 shows a backpropagation network that is currently processing the training vector [1.0 0.9 0.9], and the associated target vector is [0.1 0.9 0.1]. Let the output from unit B be 0.6 and let C be 0.8. Assume that the sigmoid is the activation function.
(a) Calculate the actual output vector.
(b) Calculate the error for each output unit.
(c) Calculate the error for each hidden unit.
(d) Calculate the weight changes for the weights connecting from unit A. Use a learning rate of 0.25.
2 Repeat Exercise 1 with a target vector [0.1 0.9 0.9].
3 Suppose that the points $\{(-1, 1), (-1, -1), (1, -1)\}$ belong to class A and that $\{(-2, -2), (1, 1), (2, 2), (4, 1)\}$ belong to class B.
(a) Show that the classes are not linearly separable.
(b) Assuming a network with units that has outputs according to

$$\text{output} = \begin{cases} 1 & \text{if total input} \geq 0 \\ 0 & \text{if total input} < 0 \end{cases}$$

show that the first layer of weights $\mathbf{W}_1$ in a three-layer network will transform the problem into a linear one. The first row in $\mathbf{W}_1$ defines the bias weights.

$$\mathbf{W}_1 = \begin{bmatrix} 1 & -6 \\ -2 & -2 \\ -1 & -3 \end{bmatrix}$$

(c) Derive a second layer of weights so that the network will correctly classify all the patterns. Assume a single output unit.

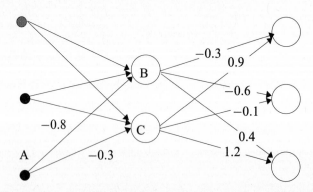

Figure 2.24 A 3-2-3 network. There are no bias units in this network.

4 The points $\{(4, -1), (8, -2), (1, 1), (3, 6)\}$ belong to class A and the points $\{(-8, 4), (-2, -3), (-1, -1), (2, -9)\}$ belong to class B. Derive a minimal network to classify these points correctly.

5 Show that the radial basis function network in Example 2.5 can solve the XOR problem with the first layer of weights set to

$$\begin{bmatrix} 0 & 1 \\ 1 & 0 \end{bmatrix}$$

6 Derive the second layer of weights for the solution to Exercise 5. Assume a bias on the output unit.

7 Define a radial basis function network to solve the XOR problem using hidden activation functions of the form $\varphi(r) \approx \sqrt{c^2 + r^2}$.

8 Repeat the forward and backward sweep of the network given in Figure 2.22 to find the new weights for the input pattern [0.9 0.9] and the target response [0.1].

9 Derive a suitable feedforward network that models the logical AND.

10 The bipolar sigmoid is another activation function that is commonly used with a backpropagation network. The function has range $(-1, 1)$ and is defined as:

$$f(x) = \frac{2}{1 + \exp(-x)} - 1$$

The derivative can be expressed as:

$$f(x) = \tfrac{1}{2}[1 + f(x)][1 - f(x)]$$

Give the error-correcting rule for both an output and a hidden unit.

11 Plot the derivative of the sigmoid function and describe how the rate at which a weight is updated relates to a unit's activation.

12 In Figure 2.25, two classes A and B are enclosed in triangular regions. A third class is considered to be defined as the intersection of A and B.

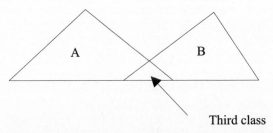

Third class

Figure 2.25 Two triangular regions and their intersection.

Propose a backpropagation network architecture for solving this task. Explain why you chose this architecture.

13 Explain why a backpropagation network has its weights initialized to both negative and positive random values as opposed to only positive values.

14 Discuss how a backpropagation network with Gaussian activation functions compares with a radial basis function network.

CHAPTER 3

Clustering patterns

Aim: To introduce unsupervised learning.

Objectives: You should be able to:

describe unsupervised learning and the principle of clustering patterns;
understand the Kohonen self-organizing network to a level that would allow you to implement this network in a language of your choice.

Prerequisites: Basic linear algebra to the level covered in Appendix A. Chapter 1.

3.1 Basic ideas

In the previous chapter we looked at supervised learning where a neural network learns to classify patterns according to instruction: a target pattern informs the network as to which class it should learn to classify an input pattern. With unsupervised learning there is no such instruction and the network is left to cluster (or group) patterns. All of the patterns within a cluster will have something in common: they will be judged as being similar. For example, suppose we are given the task of grouping furniture according to use and appearance. All chair-like objects are placed in one group and all table-like objects in another. These groups are then inspected, and the table-like group is split to separate out desks. The desk group is similar to the table-like group and so these two groups are placed close to one another away from the chair-like group. Cluster algorithms do a similar job for patterns of data. The groups are referred to as *clusters* and the arrangement of clusters should reflect two properties:

- Patterns within a cluster should be similar in some way.
- Clusters that are similar in some way should be close together.

Figure 3.1 shows a plot of two-dimensional data that fall naturally into three clusters. In Figure 3.1 a pattern point can be said to fall naturally into a cluster

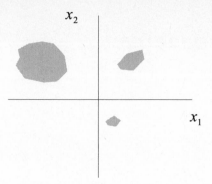

Figure 3.1 Data that form three clusters.

if it is close to a point in the same cluster compared to a point belonging to another cluster. The Euclidean squared distance is typically used to measure how close (or similar) two points are, and is given by

$$d_{pq} = \sum_i^n (x_{pi} - x_{qi})^2$$

where d_{pq} is the Euclidean squared distance between point p and point q, x_{pi} is the coordinate i for pattern p (similarly for q) and n is the number of dimensions.

If there exists a vector, $\mathbf{p}_j$ for cluster j, located at the centroid (the position that is the average of all patterns in a cluster) of each cluster in Figure 3.1 then a decision as to which cluster some vector $\mathbf{x}$ (seen as a point when plotted) belongs to is simply

$$\text{index}(\mathbf{x}) = \min d(\mathbf{p}_j, \mathbf{x}), \qquad \text{for all } j$$

which returns the index of the cluster with the lowest Euclidean squared distance from vector $\mathbf{x}$. The vectors $\mathbf{p}_j$ can be considered as prototypes for the clusters; these prototypes serve to represent the key features of a cluster. For example, if you were to cluster basketball players and horse-jockeys, no doubt the distinguishing feature would be height. So the element that denotes height in the prototype vectors of both clusters would be significantly different.

A cluster algorithm is a statistical technique for discovering clusters in a set of data. There are many clustering algorithms of varying complexity. A simple approach to clustering is to assume that a certain number of clusters exist and randomly assign the coordinates for each prototype. Each vector in the data set is then assigned to its nearest prototype and the prototype updated (moved) to become the centroid of all vectors assigned to that prototype. Figure 3.2 illustrates the idea of random prototypes that by the end of training have moved to the centre of a cluster as shown in Figure 3.3.

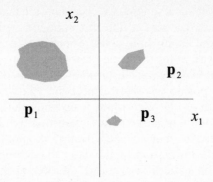

Figure 3.2 Three random vectors that will move to act as prototypes for the clusters.

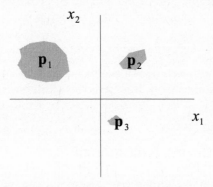

Figure 3.3 Each prototype has moved to become the centroid of a cluster.

EXAMPLE 3.1

1 Find the squared Euclidean distance between the two vectors

$$\mathbf{p} = [-2.3 \quad 1.4]$$
$$\mathbf{x} = [4.5 \quad 0.6]$$

2 Find the squared Euclidean distance between the two vectors

$$\mathbf{p} = [0.4 \quad 0.3 \quad 1.1 \quad 0.9]$$
$$\mathbf{x} = [0.6 \quad 0.7 \quad -0.5 \quad 1.1]$$

SOLUTION 3.1

1
$$d(\mathbf{p}, \mathbf{x}) = (-2.3 - 4.5)^2 + (1.4 - 0.6)^2$$
$$= 46.9$$

2 $d(\mathbf{p}, \mathbf{x}) = (0.4 - 0.6)^2 + (0.3 - 0.7)^2 + (1.1 - -0.5)^2 + (0.9 - 1.1)^2$
$$= 2.8$$

The prototypes provide a summary of the data set that is being examined. The clusters in Figure 3.1 have a different variance, with the largest cluster having a large spread along both axes. Sometimes it can be desirable to represent a cluster with more than one prototype to provide a more detailed summary of the data; to recognize clusters that are really part of a larger cluster we need to know the position of all the prototypes relative to one another. One of the difficulties with cluster algorithms is deciding the optimum number of clusters. If there are too few clusters then interesting trends in the data will be missed, and if there are too many clusters then we will not be provided with any effective summarized information of the data; the extreme case of too many clusters is where each pattern is a cluster. We could identify a number of properties we would like from a cluster algorithm:

- automatic determination of the number of prototypes;
- a measure of the similarity (or relative position) of one prototype to another;
- the key features representative of a prototype.

In practice, the first property is not really satisfied by any cluster algorithm. An unsupervised neural network that performs clustering is the self-organizing feature map (SOFM; Kohonen, 1990) developed by Kohonen in the early 1980s.

3.2 The self-organizing feature map

The SOFM has a set of input units that correspond in number to the dimension of the training vectors and output units that act as prototypes. Figure 3.4 illustrates the basic architecture. The data in Figure 3.1, for example, would require a network with two input units and at least three output units to represent each cluster.

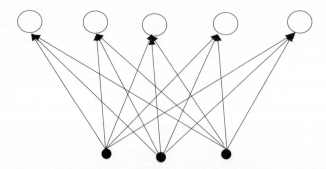

Figure 3.4 This network has three inputs and five cluster units. Each unit in the input layer is connected to every unit in the cluster layer.

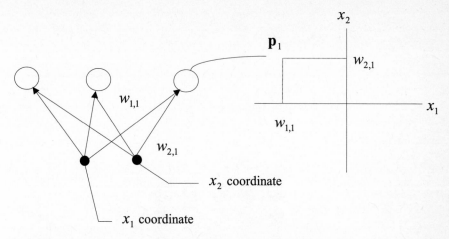

Figure 3.5 This diagram shows how a cluster unit acts as a prototype. The input layer takes coordinates from the input space. The weights adapt during training, and when learning is complete each cluster unit will have a position in the input space determined by its weights.

The input units only serve to distribute the input vector to the network's output units. The output units shall be referred to as *cluster units*. Since the number of input units matches the dimension of the input vectors and each input unit is fully connected to each cluster unit, the total number of weights impinging on a cluster unit is also the same as the dimension of the input vectors. It is often useful to consider the weights of a cluster unit as the coordinates that describe the cluster's position in the input space. Figure 3.5 shows how the weights relate to the input space.

The cluster units are arranged in a one- or two-dimensional array in the manner shown in Figure 3.6. During training all units can be considered as competing to be awarded the training vectors. When any training vector is presented, the distance to all cluster units is calculated and the unit that is closest to the training vector is denoted as the winning unit. The winning unit will then adapt its weights in a way that moves that cluster unit even closer to the training vector. It is usual for units within a pre-specified neighbourhood of the winning unit to update their weights as well. A unit is a member of the updating neighbourhood if it falls within a specified radius that is centred on the winning unit. The radius is usually reduced during learning. A learning rate determines the amount by which a cluster unit moves towards the training vector and, like the radius, it is also gradually decreased over time. We shall only be concerned with cluster units that are arranged either as a linear array or as a square grid. Other topologies can be used. Another example is a hexagon grid. The topology simply controls which units for some given radius should be updated.

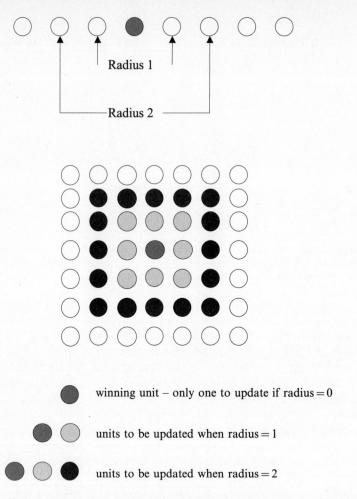

Figure 3.6 The cluster units in the top network are arranged in a linear manner, whereas the network below has the units arranged in a square grid. The topology determines which units fall within a radius of the winning unit. The units can be arranged in other ways (e.g., triangular, hexagonal) but the linear and square arrangements are typical.

It is usual to use fewer cluster units than there are training patterns because we are looking to have a summary picture of the data. At the end of training the cluster units provide a summary representation of the input pattern space. The cluster units act to map out the features of the input space. For example, later in this chapter some results of clustering the images of characters reveals that different regions of the cluster units are representative of different characters (or a mixture thereof).

3.2.1 Algorithm

In the following algorithm, η is the learning rate and n the time step.

```
initialize weights to random values.
while not HALT
    for each input vector
        for each cluster unit calculate the distance from the training vector
```

$$d_j = \sum_i (w_{ij} - x_i)^2$$

```
        find unit j with the minimum distance
        update all weight vectors for units within the radius according to
```

$$w_{ij}(n+1) = w_{ij}(n) + \eta(n)[x_i - w_{ij}(n)]$$

```
        check to see if the learning rate or radius need updating
        check HALT
```

The training vectors are selected at random from the training set. The HALT condition is met when the weight changes for all cluster units become very small; under this condition the training vectors should fall within the same region of the map from one epoch to the next.

The learning rate is varied over time. It might, for example, start at a value of 0.9 and decrease in a linear manner before remaining fixed at a small value (such as 0.01). The radius usually starts out large so that all units are initially updated. The radius also reduces over time so that in the end only a couple or possibly no neighbours of the winning unit are updated. The learning rate can also be specified to depend on how close the updating unit is to the winning unit.

EXAMPLE 3.2

1 How many epochs will it take for η to drop to 0.1 using the following update rule

$$\eta(0) = 0.90$$
$$\eta(n+1) = \eta(n) - 0.001$$

2 An SOFM has a 10×10 two-dimensional grid layout and the radius is initially set to 6. Find how many units will be updated after 1000 epochs if the winning unit is located in the extreme bottom right-hand corner of the grid and the radius is updated according to

$$r = r - 1 \text{ if current\_epoch mod } 200 = 0$$

Assume that epoch numbering starts at 1.

SOLUTION 3.2

1
$$0.1 = 0.9 - n0.001$$

$$\therefore \quad n = \frac{0.9 - 0.1}{0.001}$$

$$= 800$$

2 Assuming that epoch counting starts at 1, the radius will reduce by 1 every 200 epochs. After 1000 epochs the radius will be 1. The number of units updated will be four, including the winning unit.

3.2.2 How SOFMs learn

The feature map has two phases of learning. In the first phase the units are ordered to mirror the input space, and in the second phase fine-tuning takes place. It is common practice to illustrate the organization process using two-dimensional data so that the map can be drawn. For example, input vectors are drawn randomly from a uniform distribution contained within a square and a map trained. The map is drawn at different times during training by plotting the cluster units in the input space in the same manner as shown in Figure 3.5. The units are connected by grid lines to show their relative location. The map will usually start twisted, and gradually unfold and spread out during training. The end result of training is a map that covers the input space and is fairly regular (that is, units are almost equally spaced). A map with a square topology of 49 units was trained on 250 data points drawn from a unit square, starting with random weights that positioned each cluster unit in the centre of the input space as shown in Figure 3.7. Figures 3.8 and 3.9 show the development of the map over time.

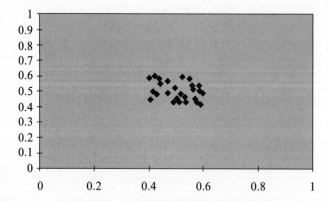

Figure 3.7 The weight vectors start with random values in the range 0.4 to 0.6.

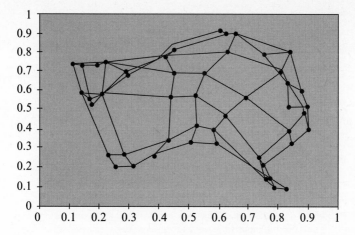

Figure 3.8 The map after 20 epochs.

As with other networks, the result of training depends on the training data and choice of learning parameters. Figure 3.10 shows the distribution of a 100 training patterns over the unit square. A map with a square topology of 25 units was trained on this data set, starting with random weights that once again positioned each unit in the centre of the input space. This is a relatively small network and not surprisingly the end result of using non-uniform data is an irregular looking map as shown Figure 3.11. The map also contains a twist in the top right-hand corner. Twists can be the result of unsuitable initial weight

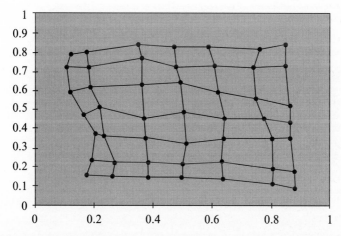

Figure 3.9 The map after 2000 epochs towards the end of training. The units are now ordered and the map will become more regular during the final phase of convergence.

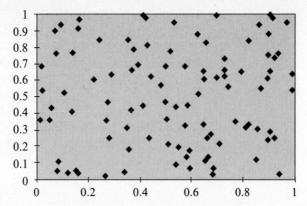

Figure 3.10 Randomly generated data. The data set is not uniform and so there are gaps –
parts of the input space are severely under-represented.

values, which determine where each cluster unit is positioned in the input space
at the start of training. For example, if the units all start out being weighted
towards one direction of the input space then the ordering process can be
hampered. Figure 3.12 shows the same experiment but this time the map is a
linear array of units. The linear array is twisting to fill the input space. The
same space-filling properties can be shown with other shapes. For example, if
the training data set is drawn uniformly from a triangle then a square map will
organize its units to fill the triangle as shown in Figure 3.13.

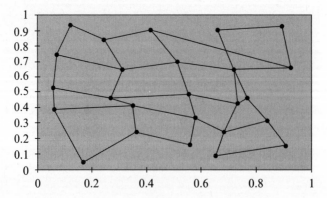

Figure 3.11 The map unit locations after training on the data shown in Figure 3.10. Adjacent
units are connected by grid lines.

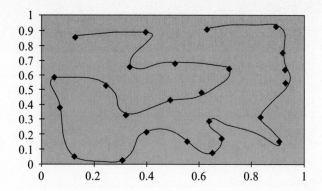

Figure 3.12 A linear map of 25 units fitting random data drawn from a unit square.

Hecht-Nielsen (1990) gives a similar two-dimensional mapping example, but this time the task is to map the angular movements of a robot's arm to (x, y) coordinates. An experiment with a robot arm is presented next.

A square map will be used to represent the (x, y) coordinates of a robot's gripper, with adjacent units representing adjacent coordinates. You can think of the map as mirroring the squares on a chessboard (or part thereof,

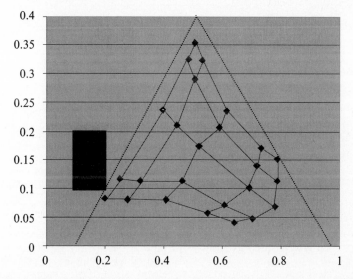

Figure 3.13. The SOFM square grid is gradually forming itself into a triangular region. The training data were sampled from the hatched area and the net's weights were randomized before training so that all units were positioned within the black rectangle.

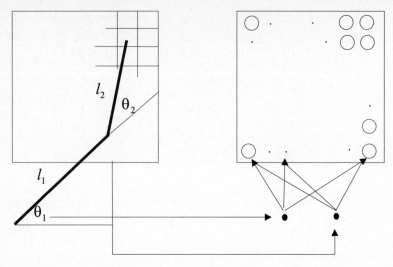

Figure 3.14 The task illustrated is to map the angle of each arm segment to positions on the grid. If the arm is to move, for example, to the top right-hand corner then the top right-hand unit's weight vector will contain the angles with which to position the arm. Think of pressing the unit where the arm tip is to move to. The unit then issues the relevant angles.

depending on the number of units used). The idea is shown in Figure 3.14. The relationship between the angles and the coordinates is given by

$$x = l_1 \cos \theta_1 + l_2 \cos(\theta_1 + \theta_2)$$

$$y = l_1 \sin \theta_1 + l_2 \sin(\theta_1 + \theta_2)$$

$$\theta_2 = \cos^{-1}\left(\frac{x^2 + y^2 + l_1^2 + l_2^2}{2l_1l_2}\right)$$

$$\theta_1 = \tan^{-1}(y/x) - \tan^{-1}\left(\frac{l_2 \sin \theta_2}{l_1 + l_2 \cos \theta_2}\right)$$

The relationship is nonlinear but (x, y) coordinates that are adjacent will have similar angles.

The results presented are from a single trial with no attempt at improvement; it is anticipated that better results could emerge with some experimenting. The robot's arm was pivoted as shown in Figure 3.15. A very small training set was generated to include 25 points $\{(4, 1), (4, 2), (4, 3), (4, 4), (4, 5), (5, 1), (5, 2), (5, 3), (5, 4), (5, 5), \ldots, (8, 5)\}$. The angles to put the tip of the robot's arm at these points were then calculated and used to train an SOFM. It is normal practice to use a much lower number of units than training points since the

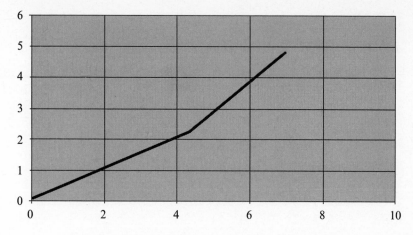

Figure 3.15 The robot's arm positioned in the grid space.

basic aim of an SOFM is to summarize the input space with a number of prototypes. In this experiment, though, the reverse was done and a square map was chosen that contained 49 units. The idea was to try and ensure that no more than a single training point would be assigned to any particular unit and to see how the units would spread out to cover the input space. The weights started at small random values. The results are summarized in Figures 3.16 to 3.18. Figure 3.18 shows that for each training pattern there is a representative

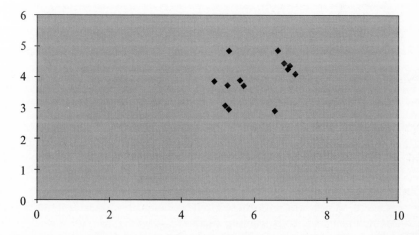

Figure 3.16 The weight vector positions converted to (x, y) coordinates after 5000 cycles through all the training data.

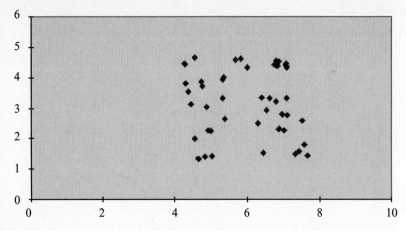

Figure 3.17 The weight vector positions converted to (x, y) coordinates after 10 000 cycles through all the training data.

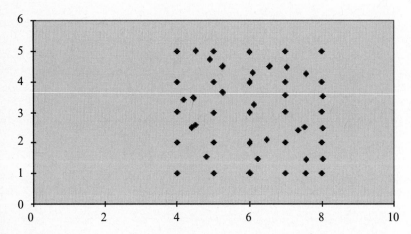

Figure 3.18 The weight vector positions converted to (x, y) coordinates after 20 000 cycles through all the training data.

unit. Furthermore, many of the unassigned units have spread out to occupy intermediate positions of the input space.

EXAMPLE 3.3

An SOFM network with three input units and four cluster units is to be trained using the four training vectors:

$$[0.8 \quad 0.7 \quad 0.4], \quad [0.6 \quad 0.9 \quad 0.9], \quad [0.3 \quad 0.4 \quad 0.1], \quad [0.1 \quad 0.1 \quad 0.3]$$

and initial weights

$$\begin{bmatrix} 0.5 & 0.4 \\ 0.6 & 0.2 \\ 0.8 & 0.5 \end{bmatrix}$$

The initial radius is 0 and the learning rate η is 0.5. Calculate the weight changes during the first cycle through the data, taking the training vectors in the given order.

SOLUTION 3.3

For input vector 1 we have, for cluster unit 1,

$$d_1 = (0.5 - 0.8)^2 + (0.6 - 0.7)^2 + (0.8 - 0.4)^2 = 0.26$$

and for cluster unit 2,

$$d_2 = (0.4 - 0.8)^2 + (0.2 - 0.7)^2 + (0.5 - 0.4)^2 = 0.42$$

Unit 1 is closest and so

$$w_{ij}(n+1) = w_{ij}(n) + 0.5[x_i - w_{ij}(n)]$$

The new weights are

$$\begin{bmatrix} 0.65 & 0.4 \\ 0.65 & 0.2 \\ 0.6 & 0.5 \end{bmatrix}$$

For input vector 2 we have, for cluster unit 1,

$$d_1 = (0.65 - 0.6)^2 + (0.65 - 0.9)^2 + (0.60 - 0.9)^2 = 0.155$$

and for cluster unit 2

$$d_2 = (0.4 - 0.6)^2 + (0.2 - 0.9)^2 + (0.5 - 0.9)^2 = 0.69$$

Unit 1 is closest and so the new weights are

$$\begin{bmatrix} 0.625 & 0.400 \\ 0.775 & 0.200 \\ 0.750 & 0.500 \end{bmatrix}$$

For input vector 3 we have, for cluster unit 1

$$d_1 = (0.625 - 0.3)^2 + (0.775 - 0.4)^2 + (0.75 - 0.1)^2 = 0.67$$

and for cluster unit 2,

$$d_2 = (0.4 - 0.3)^2 + (0.2 - 0.4)^2 + (0.5 - 0.1)^2 = 0.21$$

Unit 2 is closest and so the new weights are

$$\begin{bmatrix} 0.625 & 0.350 \\ 0.775 & 0.300 \\ 0.750 & 0.300 \end{bmatrix}$$

For input vector 4 we have, for cluster unit 1,

$$d_1 = (0.625 - 0.1)^2 + (0.775 - 0.1)^2 + (0.75 - 0.3)^3 = 0.93$$

and for cluster unit 2,

$$d_2 = (0.35 - 0.10)^2 + (0.30 - 0.10)^2 + (0.30 - 0.30)^2 = 0.10$$

Unit 2 is closest and so the new weights are

$$\begin{bmatrix} 0.625 & 0.225 \\ 0.775 & 0.200 \\ 0.750 & 0.300 \end{bmatrix}$$

3.2.3 Some further points regarding SOFMs

Sometimes it is useful to the use the angle between vectors as the measure of similarity. Consider Figure 3.19. The vector $\mathbf{a}$ is closer to the prototype $\mathbf{p}_1$ in terms of Euclidean distance but closer to prototype $\mathbf{p}_2$ in terms of angle. The *dot product*, which is sometimes called the *inner product* or *scalar product*, of the vectors

$$\mathbf{v} = [v_1 \quad v_2 \quad \ldots \quad v_n] \quad \text{and} \quad \mathbf{w} = [w_1 \quad w_2 \quad \ldots \quad w_n]$$

is given by

$$\mathbf{v} \cdot \mathbf{w} = [v_1 w_1 \quad v_2 w_2 \quad \ldots \quad v_n w_n]$$

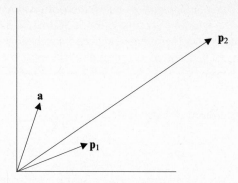

Figure 3.19 The three vectors used for Example 3.4.

The angle between non-zero vectors $\mathbf{v}$ and $\mathbf{w}$ is

$$\cos^{-1}\left(\frac{\mathbf{v} \cdot \mathbf{w}}{\|\mathbf{v}\|\|\mathbf{w}\|}\right)$$

The norm or magnitude of the vector is $\|\mathbf{v}\| = \sqrt{v_1^2 + v_2^2 + \cdots + v_n^2}$. A vector can be normalized to unit length by dividing each of its elements by its norm. If the vectors are normalized, the winning prototype index for an input pattern is given by

$$\text{index}(\mathbf{x}) = \max\{\mathbf{p}_j \cdot \mathbf{x}\} \qquad \text{for all } j$$

Training an SOFM, when using the dot product to judge similarity, proceeds as before except the weight updates are given by

$$\mathbf{w}_j(n+1) + \frac{\mathbf{w}_j(n) + \eta\mathbf{x}}{\|\mathbf{w}_j(n) + \eta\mathbf{x}\|}$$

So the winning unit has its weight vector changed by adding some fraction of the input vector and then normalizing.

EXAMPLE 3.4

Let the vectors in Figure 3.19 be

$$\mathbf{a} = [1 \quad 4]$$
$$\mathbf{p}_1 = [2 \quad 1]$$
$$\mathbf{p}_2 = [6 \quad 6]$$

(a) Show that **a** is closer to $\mathbf{p}_2$ using the dot product.
(b) If $\mathbf{p}_2$ is the winning prototype in an SOFM, show how $\mathbf{p}_2$ moves assuming that **a** is presented twice in succession (that is, treat the problem as if no other training patterns exist). Let $\eta = 1$.

SOLUTION 3.4

(a) The normalized dot products are

$$\mathbf{ap}_1^T = \frac{(1 \times 2) + (4 \times 1)}{\sqrt{1^2 + 4^2}\sqrt{2^2 + 2^2}} = 0.651$$

$$\mathbf{ap}_2^T = \frac{(1 \times 6) + (4 \times 6)}{\sqrt{1^2 + 4^2}\sqrt{6^2 + 6^2}} = 0.857$$

So $\mathbf{p}_2$ is closer. Note that $\mathbf{ap}_j^T$ is used here to denote the normalized product, where the superscript denotes the transpose of a vector.

(b) The normalized vectors are

$$\mathbf{a} = \begin{bmatrix} 1/\sqrt{17} & 4/\sqrt{17} \end{bmatrix}$$

$$\mathbf{p}_2 = \begin{bmatrix} 6/\sqrt{72} & 6/\sqrt{72} \end{bmatrix}$$

For the first presentation

$$\mathbf{p}_2(n+1) = \frac{\begin{bmatrix} 6/\sqrt{72} + 1/\sqrt{17} & 6/\sqrt{72} + 4/\sqrt{17} \end{bmatrix}}{\sqrt{\left(6/\sqrt{72} + 1/\sqrt{17}\right)^2 + \left(6/\sqrt{72} + 4/\sqrt{17}\right)^2}}$$

$$= [0.493 \quad 0.870]$$

For the second presentation

$$\mathbf{p}_2(n+2) = \frac{\begin{bmatrix} 0.493 + 1/\sqrt{17} & 0.870 + 4/\sqrt{17} \end{bmatrix}}{\left(0.493 + 1/\sqrt{17}\right)^2 + \left(0.870 + 4/\sqrt{17}\right)^2}$$

$$= [0.371 \quad 0.928]$$

Kohonen (1990) gives a few practical hints for training an SOFM. During the first 1000 iterations the learning rate should start out close to unity, thereafter gradually decreasing. The exact method of decreasing the learning rate is not critical and can be linear, exponential or inversely proportional to the number of iterations. The ordering of the map occurs during this initial phase. After the ordering phase the learning rate should be maintained at a small value (say, 0.1 or less) for a long period whilst fine adjustment of the map takes place. The radius should start out large (for example, it can be greater than half the diameter of the map) and should decrease linearly during the first 1000 iterations, after which the radius can be maintained at one or zero. There should be a large number of iterations, typically between 10 000 and 100 000.

3.3 An experiment

In Chapter 2, we managed to train a feedforward network using supervised training to recognize the four characters {A, B, C, D} in three different fonts. The training characters are shown again in Figure 3.20. We shall now review an experiment using the same nine training patterns.

The experiment was designed simply to see how an SOFM would cluster the training instances. A square grid with nine units in total was chosen. The initial radius was set at 3 and the learning rate at 1. The network was trained for 3000 cycles through all the patterns. Table 3.1 shows how the characters clustered at the end of training. Each cell in the table corresponds to a unit in the grid.

The character images are 16×16 pixel grids, and so there are 256 inputs to each unit. After the network has converged, we expect a unit to be a prototype for the patterns that get assigned to that unit. If we plot the weight vectors as an image, we might expect a unit's image to look similar to the patterns for which it is a prototype. The procedure for plotting is easy. The original bitmaps of the characters used 0 to represent a white pixel and 1 for a black pixel. Therefore all unit weights will have values between 0 and 1. Each weight is associated with a single pixel in the original grid and so we can view each

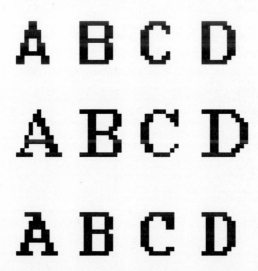

Figure 3.20 Each row of characters is drawn in a different font.

Table 3.1 *The SOFM units to which the characters have been labelled: the numbers denote different fonts*

A1 A2 A3		B1 D1 B3 D3
B2 D2		C1 C2 C3

weight as a grey-scale value between 0 and 1 (grey scales actually range from 0 to 255 and so the weights have to be scaled to the same range). From examination of Figure 3.21, which shows the images of each unit's weights, you can see to which unit a pattern is likely to be assigned. In this experiment all the As have clustered together and so have all the Cs. The Bs and Ds have similar shapes and have clustered together. Ideally, we might hope for the Bs and Ds also to cluster against separate units. However, for real-world problems clustering gives an indication of similarity and is not meant to be foolproof.

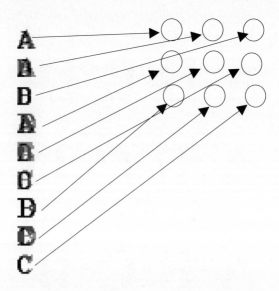

Figure 3.21 The figure shows unit weights plotted as grey-scale values.

Besides, even we categorize objects differently depending on context. For instance, book-ends might be considered office equipment or perhaps as ornaments if designed with appearance in mind. The network has shown us something about the characters without our having to tell the network anything about these characters (the network was not supervised). The network has told us that six of the patterns (the As and Cs) fall into two very distinct groups. Of course, being animals with good vision, we are masters at recognizing the similarity of images. The point, however, is that we might be analyzing data that have very many features and cannot be visualized in such a simple way. If we do not know how to classify such data, a network like Kohonen's self-organizing map can prove very useful.

3.4 Summary

A neural network can be made to cluster data by a process of competition. A network's units can also be made to undergo a self-organization process so that the network's units, when drawn in the input space, mimic the topology of the training data. Two forms of similarity measure are commonly used: Euclidean distance between vectors and the angle between vectors.

A self-organizing feature map has the following properties:

- All cluster units connect to the input units. The input units serve to distribute the input features of a pattern to all cluster units.
- During training, units compete for a pattern. The winning unit, which is the unit closest to the input pattern, adapts its weights so that it becomes closer (more similar) to the current input pattern.
- There are two phases of learning. During the first phase units that are neighbours of the winning unit are allowed to update their weights. The neighbourhood of units that are allowed to update their weights decreases during the first phase. During the second phase, all weights are adjusted by small amounts until the network converges.
- Once trained, the network can be used to classify an unknown pattern on the basis of its similarity to patterns with which the network was trained with.

3.5 Further reading

Kohonen (1990) provides some interesting examples of the self-organization process and practical hints in using SOFMs. Kohonen's paper is also a good source for locating other studies with SOFMs. Hecht-Nielsen (1990) gives a good overview of competitive learning. Adaptive resonance theory is another form of clustering network with wide applications; it was developed by Carpenter and Grossberg (1987) but for a good introduction see Fausett (1994).

3.6 Exercises

1 The vectors $\mathbf{x}$, $\mathbf{p}_1$ and $\mathbf{p}_2$ are given by

$$\mathbf{x} = [0.2 \quad -1.4 \quad 2.3]$$
$$\mathbf{p}_1 = [0.6 \quad -4.0 \quad 7.0]$$
$$\mathbf{p}_2 = [0.1 \quad -1.0 \quad 2.2]$$

(a) Which prototype is $\mathbf{x}$ nearest to in terms of Euclidean distance?
(b) Which prototype is $\mathbf{x}$ nearest to in terms of the dot product?
(c) Adapt the weight vector of the winning prototype in (a) according to the SOFM learning algorithm with a learning rate of 0.8.
(d) Adapt the weight vector of the winning prototype in (b) according to the SOFM learning for the dot product with a learning rate of 0.8.

2 Repeat Question 1 for the following vectors:

$$\mathbf{x} = [0.2 \quad -1.4 \quad -0.3 \quad 0.8]$$
$$\mathbf{p}_1 = [0.3 \quad -3.0 \quad 1.0 \quad 0.2]$$
$$\mathbf{p}_2 = [0.4 \quad -1.4 \quad -2.0 \quad 3.0]$$

3 The rate of learning in an SOFM decays during the first 1000 iterations according to the law

$$\eta(n) = 0.15\left(1 - \frac{n}{1000}\right)$$

where n is the iteration.

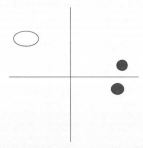

Figure 3.22 Two clusters of data and prototypes for an SOFM.

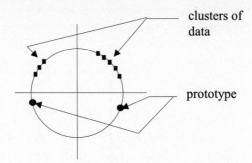

Figure 3.23 Vectors on the unit circle.

(a) How many iterations will it take for the learning rate to fall to 0.003?

(b) Why is this law not a good choice?

4 The Figure 3.22 shows two clusters of data (shaded). The unshaded region in the top left-hand quadrant contains a number of prototypes (unit weight vectors) as the initial states for an SOFM. Assuming a radius of zero, explain what might happen with the organization of the feature map if trained on this data.

5 The vectors in Figure 3.23 all lie on the unit circle. Assuming that the vectors will always be made to lie on this circle, will there be a difference in judging the winning prototype between using the Euclidean distance and using the dot product? Explain your reasoning.

6 Show that, for a vector $\mathbf{x}$, finding the winning unit using the minimum Euclidean distance criterion is the same as using the maximum dot product criterion for normalized vectors. (*Hint*: The winning unit using the Euclidean metric can be expressed as $\min\{\|\mathbf{x} - \mathbf{p}_j\|\}$. Expand the expression and compare with the normalized definition of the dot product).

7 A linear SOFM with three units was trained on the XOR problem using 0.1 and 0.9 for 0 and 1 respectively for the four training patterns. The SOFM was trained using the dot product and the final weights are listed below. Find how the patterns cluster.

Unit 1	Unit 2	Unit 3
0.110	0.707	0.994
0.994	0.707	0.110

8 The MAXNET (see Lippmann, 1987) is a competitive neural network that can be used to find the network unit whose input is the largest. Each unit connects to every other unit with bidirectional weights and a unit connects to itself. All weights are set equal apart from the self-connections which are set to 1:

$$w_{ij} = \begin{cases} 1 & \text{if } i = j \\ -\omega & \text{if } i \neq j \end{cases}$$

where $0 < \omega < 1/N$ and N is the number of network units.

The activation of a unit is set equal to its input provided the input is greater than zero, otherwise the activation is set to zero. A unit receives a weighted signal from every other unit and from itself. A unit does not actually change its activation until the end of an iteration. Each unit continually updates until no more than one unit has a nonzero activation.

Figure 3.24 shows activations of three units, and the weights have been initialized according to the above rule.

For the first iteration, the input to the first unit is $0.5 + 0.2 \times -0.5 + 0.6 \times -0.5 = 0.1$. The new activation is 0.1 since the input is greater than zero. The unit maintains the activation of 0.5 until the end of the first iteration. The input to second unit is $0.2 + 0.5 \times -0.5 + 0.6 \times -0.5 = -0.35$. The new activation is 0 since the input is less than zero. The unit maintains the activation of 0.2 until the end of the first iteration. The input to third unit is $0.6 + 0.5 \times -0.5 + 0.2 \times -0.5 = 0.25$. The new activation is 0.25 since the input is greater than zero. All units can now change activation.

For the second iteration, the input to unit 1 is $0.1 + 0 + 0.25 \times -0.5 = -0.025$. So the new activation at the end of the iteration will be zero. The input to unit 2 must be less than zero. The input to unit 3 is $0.25 + 0.1 \times -0.5 + 0 = 0.2$. The only unit with a non-zero activation is unit 3. So the process stops and unit 3 is the winner.

Repeat the above example using activations of 0.7, 0.6, 0.3, respectively.

9 Show how a MAXNET could be applied to Question 8 to indicate the winning unit.

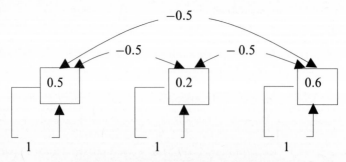

Figure 3.24 The activations of three units.

10 A MAXNET consists of eight units. Sketch the network and mark on it appropriate weights. Show that the network will operate as desired for a combination of activations that you specify.

11 If an SOFM is constructed using a hexagonal grid, assuming that the winning unit is the unit in the centre of the grid, how many units will be updated if the radius is 1, and how many units will be updated if the radius is 2?

CHAPTER 4

Pattern association

Aim: To introduce associative memory.

Objectives: You should be able to:

describe the difference between autoassociative and heteroassociative networks;
understand the discrete Hopfield network and the bidirectional associative network to a level that enables you to simulate them using a spreadsheet program or in a language of your choice;
describe how a backpropagation network can be used for autoassociation;
explain how data compression can be achieved using the autoassociative backpropagation network.

Prerequisites: Basic linear algebra to a level given in Appendix A. Chapter 1.

4.1 Introduction

We are all familiar with the idea of association: an English word may have an associated French word; we may associate a name with the photograph of a friend; and we may even manage to associate a faded picture of some object with the real thing. In Chapter 2, a form of associative learning was introduced where for each training pattern there was a desired output pattern. In this chapter we are concerned with memorizing pattern pairs. The idea is that we can recall from memory a complete pattern even if we do not have all the information to hand to start the search for the stored pattern. For example, you want to locate a book in a library but do not remember the title; instead you have available the author's name and a description of subject matter which is sufficient (hopefully!) to retrieve the associated item.

When a pair of associated patterns are to be stored and both patterns are the same, the memory is known as *autoassociative* whereas if both patterns are different the memory is known as *heteroassociative*. This chapter will look at three neural network models for associating patterns.

4.2 The discrete Hopfield network

The Hopfield network is an autoassociative network that acts like a memory and can recall a stored pattern even when cued (that is, presented as input) with a noisy version of that pattern. For example, the network may store a series of letter characters, and if the network is presented with a noisy version of a stored character it should be capable of retrieving the clean version. The discrete Hopfield network has the following characteristics:

- A single layer of units (input units that present an initial input pattern are not included).
- All units connect to every other unit, but a unit does not connect to itself.
- Only one unit updates at a time – unlike a backpropagation network, for example, where every unit in a layer could update simultaneously if implemented in parallel hardware.
- Units are updated in random order, but each unit must be updated at the same average rate. In other words, for a network with 10 units, after 100 updates each unit should have updated on approximately 10 occasions.
- The output of a unit is restricted to 0 or 1.

The Hopfield network is recurrent in that, for a given input pattern, the network's output is recirculated as input until a stable state is reached. An example of a Hopfield network is shown in Figure 4.1. It is easier to think of the Hopfield network as having no input units since an input vector simply defines the initial activation of each unit. For example, the inputs are binary and so an input vector [1 1 0 1] means that the acivation for units {1, 2, 4} will be 1 and for {3} the activation will be 0. A unit is updated when all other units broadcast their activations along the impinging weighted connections and the usual summation of products is then calculated (the dot product is taken); a unit's activation is calculated using an activation rule. Each unit in a Hopfield

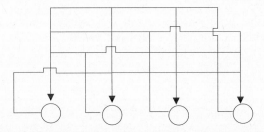

Figure 4.1 A Hopfield network with four units. There is a unit for each element in the input vector. Every unit connects to every other unit but a unit does not connect to itself. Connections are bidirectional.

network has a state which is simply the activation value that would be sent to other units, and at any point in time the state of the network is the vector of all unit states.

Binary inputs can be used with the Hopfield network but the presentation given here will use $+1$ to denote an 'on' state for a unit and -1 to denote an 'off' state. The net input to a unit is calculated as:

$$net_j = \sum_{i=1}^{n} s_i w_{ij}$$

where s_i is the state of unit i. When a unit is updated it will have its state modified according to the rule

$$s_j = \begin{cases} +1 & \text{if } net_j > 0 \\ -1 & \text{if } net_j < 0 \end{cases}$$

The above relation is known as the *signum* function and can be abbreviated to

$$s_j = \text{sgn}(net_j)$$

If the net input is zero then the unit stays in the state it was in prior to the update.

The operation of the network is very simple. An input vector provides the initial state of each unit. A unit is selected at random to be updated. The selected unit receives a weighted signal from all other units and updates its state. Another unit is selected and the process repeated. The network has converged when no unit changes state if selected for updating.

The weights for a Hopfield network are determined directly from the training data without the need for training in the more conventional sense. The Hopfield network acts as a memory and the procedure for storing a single vector is to take the outer product of the vector with itself. This procedure produces a matrix which defines the weights for a Hopfield network provided all of the diagonal elements have been set to zero (because the diagonal elements define the self-connections and a unit does not connect to itself). So the weight matrix to store a vector $\mathbf{x}$ is given by:

$$\mathbf{W} = \mathbf{x}^T\mathbf{x}$$

EXAMPLE 4.1

Find the weights of a Hopfield network to store the pattern:

$$[1 \quad -1 \quad 1 \quad 1]$$

SOLUTION 4.1

$$\begin{bmatrix} 1 \\ -1 \\ 1 \\ 1 \end{bmatrix} \begin{bmatrix} 1 & -1 & 1 & 1 \end{bmatrix} = \begin{bmatrix} 1 & -1 & 1 & 1 \\ -1 & 1 & -1 & -1 \\ 1 & -1 & 1 & 1 \\ 1 & -1 & 1 & 1 \end{bmatrix}$$

So the weights are:

$$\mathbf{W} = \begin{bmatrix} 0 & -1 & 1 & 1 \\ -1 & 0 & -1 & -1 \\ 1 & -1 & 0 & 1 \\ 1 & -1 & 1 & 0 \end{bmatrix}$$

The first column lists all the weights connecting to the first unit, column 2 the second unit, etc. If the network is cued with the pattern [1 −1 1 1], all units in this instance will remain in the same state after updating. The cue defines the initial state of each unit, so in this example the second unit has state −1 and all others have state 1. The first unit is updated by multiplying the cue vector with the first column in the weight matrix:

$$\begin{bmatrix} 1 & -1 & 1 & 1 \end{bmatrix} \begin{bmatrix} 0 \\ -1 \\ 1 \\ 1 \end{bmatrix} = 3, \qquad \text{sgn}(3) = 1$$

So the first unit stays in the same state, and so would all other units if they were also updated.

EXAMPLE 4.2

Find the stable state of the Hopfield network in Example 4.1 when cued with the pattern:

$$\begin{bmatrix} -1 & -1 & 1 & 1 \end{bmatrix}$$

SOLUTION 4.2

The units should be updated in random order. For illustration, the units are updated in order 3, 4, 1, 2. First, unit 3:

$$\begin{bmatrix} -1 & -1 & 1 & 1 \end{bmatrix} \begin{bmatrix} 1 \\ -1 \\ 0 \\ 1 \end{bmatrix} = 1, \qquad \text{sgn}(1) = 1$$

So unit 3 remains in the same state. Next, unit 4:

$$[-1 \quad -1 \quad 1 \quad 1]\begin{bmatrix} 1 \\ -1 \\ 1 \\ 0 \end{bmatrix} = 1, \qquad \text{sgn}(1) = 1$$

So, unit 4 remains in the same state. Now, unit 1:

$$[-1 \quad -1 \quad 1 \quad 1]\begin{bmatrix} 0 \\ -1 \\ 1 \\ 1 \end{bmatrix} = 3, \qquad \text{sgn}(3) = 1$$

So unit 1 changes state from -1 to 1. Finally, unit 2:

$$[1 \quad -1 \quad 1 \quad 1]\begin{bmatrix} -1 \\ 0 \\ -1 \\ -1 \end{bmatrix} = -3, \qquad \text{sgn}(-3) = -1$$

So unit 2 stays in the same state. We see that the original stored vector, which is a stable state of the network, has been recovered. We should really check to make sure of the stable state by updating all of the units again and making sure that there is no change of state.

The procedure for storing more than a single pattern in a Hopfield network is straightforward: the outer product is found for each vector and all resulting weight matrices are added.

EXAMPLE 4.3

Define the Hopfield weight matrix to store the two vectors:

$$[-1 \quad 1 \quad -1]$$
$$[1 \quad -1 \quad 1]$$

SOLUTION 4.3

The weight matrix is

$$\mathbf{W} = \begin{bmatrix} -1 \\ 1 \\ -1 \end{bmatrix}[-1 \quad 1 \quad -1] + \begin{bmatrix} 1 \\ -1 \\ 1 \end{bmatrix}[1 \quad -1 \quad 1]$$

$$= \begin{bmatrix} 1 & -1 & 1 \\ -1 & 1 & -1 \\ 1 & -1 & 1 \end{bmatrix} + \begin{bmatrix} 1 & -1 & 1 \\ -1 & 1 & -1 \\ 1 & -1 & 1 \end{bmatrix}$$

$$= \begin{bmatrix} 0 & -2 & 2 \\ -2 & 0 & -2 \\ 2 & -2 & 0 \end{bmatrix}$$

The diagonal elements have been zeroed.

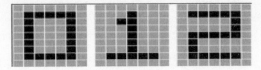

Figure 4.2 Three patterns stored by a Hopfield network. A black pixel is recorded as 1 and a grey one as −1.

EXPERIMENT

A Hopfield network was used to store the three patterns shown in Figure 4.2. Each pattern was treated as a string of bipolar values, with 1 representing black and −1 representing grey. A string has 63 elements, and so there were 63 units in the network and $63 \times 63 - 63$ weights (the number of weights from the outer product minus the zeroed diagonal elements). Once the weights were defined a noisy version of the digit '1' was used to cue the network. The pattern that emerged over a number of iterations is shown in Figure 4.3.

The above experiment demonstrated the correct recovery of a stored pattern when given a noisy version of that pattern. Sometimes a Hopfield network will settle into an incorrect state, such as recovering the wrong pattern or settling on a distorted version of the correct pattern (so that the recovered pattern may be recognizable but still has some noise).

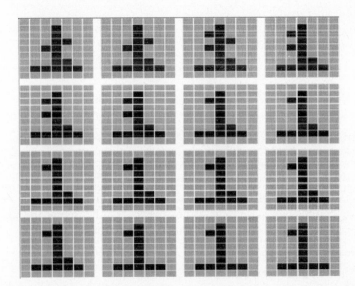

Figure 4.3 The cue pattern appears in the first frame in the top left-hand corner. Each frame represents ten iterations of the network (that is, ten random updates). The order of progression is from left to right and from top to bottom.

Table 4.1 *Energy changes as a unit's state changes*

Old s_j	$\sum s_i w_{ij}$	New s_j	Δs_j	Energy change
pos	pos	pos	pos	neg
pos	neg	neg	neg	neg
neg	neg	neg	neg	neg
neg	pos	pos	pos	neg

A number of people have derived guidelines for the number of patterns that can be stored in a Hopfield network. One such guideline is given by Haykin (1994) as

$$p_{\max} = \frac{N}{2 \ln N}$$

which is the maximum number of patterns that can be stored if most patterns are to have perfect recall; N is the number of network units.

4.2.1 Energy function

Hopfield (1984) proved that his network would converge to a stable pattern of activation by defining an energy function for the system. In our presentation, a unit changes state according to a threshold of zero, and therefore we can present a simplified version of Hopfield's energy function, similar to that given by Haykin (1994):

$$E = -\frac{1}{2} \sum_j \sum_i s_j s_i w_{ij}$$

If a unit j changes state by Δs_j the change in energy is:

$$\Delta E = -\Delta s_j \sum_i s_i w_{ij}$$

We can consider how this energy changes as a function of Δs_j and $\sum s_i w_{ij}$. Table 4.1 shows that the sign of Δs_j is the same as $\sum s_i w_{ij}$, and therefore the energy will always decrease on successive iterations. For example, the first row shows that if a unit is in a positive state and its net input is greater than zero (positive) then the new state remains positive and so the change in state will be positive and the energy change therefore will be negative.

4.3 Bidirectional associative memory

A network that has much in common with the Hopfield network is the bidirectional associative memory (BAM) developed by Kosko (1988). A BAM

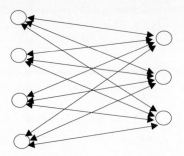

Figure 4.4 A bidirectional associative memory. The units on the left represent patterns of dimension 4, while those on the right represent the associated patterns of dimension 3.

is a heteroassociative recurrent network. The network stores pattern pairs, and it can recall a pattern when its associated pattern is presented as a cue. There are two layers of units, one for each pattern in a pair, and both layers are connected with weights that are bidirectional (that is, can pass activation in both directions); see Figure 4.4.

Only the discrete bipolar BAM is considered here, but there is a version that handles continuous values. To store a pattern **s**, with an associated pattern **t**, the outer product is taken to define the weights. The procedure is the same as for the Hopfield network, except that the matrix need not be square and the diagonal elements are not zeroed. The weight matrix for a single pair is:

$$\mathbf{W} = \mathbf{s}^T \mathbf{t}$$

The weights from each product are summed to store more than a single pair in the same manner used for the Hopfield network.

The procedure for recalling an item is similar to that for the Hopfield network. In the following description, i is one layer of units and j is the associated layer of units.

- Set the activations of the i layer to the cue pattern.
- Propagate activation to the j layer. The net input to a unit in the j layer is

$$net_j = \sum_i s_i w_{ij}$$

- Calculate the new state for each unit in the j layer:

$$t_j = f(net_j)$$

- Propagate activation to the i layer. The net input to a unit in the i layer is

$$net_i = \sum_j s_j w_{ji}$$

- Calculate the new state for each unit in the i layer:

$$s_i = f(net_i)$$

- Repeat this two-way propagation of activation signals until a stable state is reached. The activation for each layer is defined relative to a threshold θ:

$$t_j = f(net_j) = \begin{cases} 1 & \text{if } net_j > \theta_j \\ t_j & \text{if } net_j = \theta_j \\ -1 & \text{if } net_j < \theta_j \end{cases}$$

$$s_i = f(net_i) = \begin{cases} 1 & \text{if } net_i > \theta_i \\ s_i & \text{if } net_i = \theta_i \\ -1 & \text{if } net_i < \theta_i \end{cases}$$

All units in the network start with zero activation. Note that propagation can start from either layer since s might be used to recall t or vice versa.

EXAMPLE 4.4

1 Three patterns (the images for 1, 2, and 3) shown in Figure 4.5 are to be stored in a bipolar BAM. Their associated patterns are the numbers in three-bit binary (converted to bipolar) form. Table 4.2 shows the associated patterns. Devise the weights for the BAM.
2 Show that each association can be recalled.

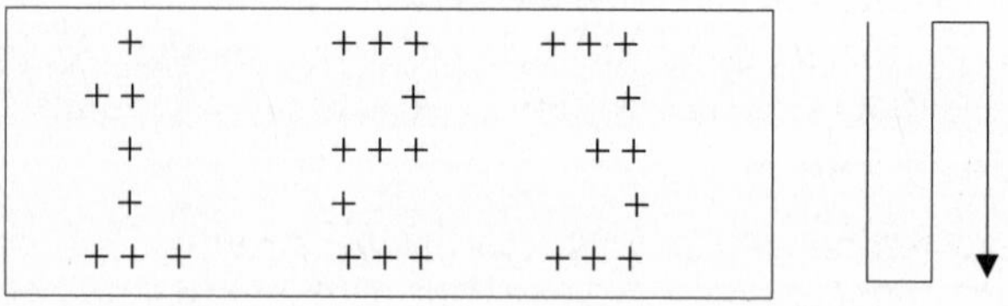

+	+ + +	+ + +
+ +	+	+
+	+ + +	+ +
+	+	+
+ + +	+ + +	+ + +

Figure 4.5 Each digit is on a 5 × 3 grid. A blank is denoted by −1 and a '+' by +1. The digits are represented by a linear array working from top to bottom and from left to right.

Table 4.2 *The digits {1, 2, 3} are associated with bipolar patterns*

Pattern	Associated pattern		
1	−1	−1	1
2	−1	1	−1
3	−1	1	1

SOLUTION 4.4

1

$$\mathbf{W} = \begin{bmatrix} -1 \\ 1 \\ -1 \\ -1 \\ 1 \\ 1 \\ 1 \\ 1 \\ 1 \\ 1 \\ -1 \\ -1 \\ -1 \\ -1 \\ 1 \end{bmatrix} \begin{bmatrix} -1 & -1 & 1 \end{bmatrix} + \begin{bmatrix} 1 \\ -1 \\ 1 \\ 1 \\ 1 \\ 1 \\ -1 \\ 1 \\ -1 \\ 1 \\ 1 \\ 1 \\ 1 \\ -1 \\ 1 \end{bmatrix} \begin{bmatrix} -1 & 1 & -1 \end{bmatrix} + \begin{bmatrix} 1 \\ -1 \\ -1 \\ -1 \\ 1 \\ 1 \\ -1 \\ 1 \\ -1 \\ 1 \\ 1 \\ 1 \\ 1 \\ 1 \\ 1 \end{bmatrix} \begin{bmatrix} -1 & 1 & 1 \end{bmatrix}$$

$$\therefore \quad \mathbf{W} = \begin{bmatrix} -1 & 3 & -1 \\ 1 & -3 & 1 \\ 1 & 1 & -3 \\ 1 & 1 & -3 \\ -3 & 1 & 1 \\ -3 & 1 & 1 \\ 1 & -3 & 1 \\ -3 & 1 & 1 \\ 1 & -3 & 1 \\ -3 & 1 & 1 \\ -1 & 3 & -1 \\ -1 & 3 & -1 \\ -1 & 3 & -1 \\ 1 & 1 & 1 \\ -3 & 1 & 1 \end{bmatrix}$$

2 The binary pattern for the digitized image of '2' shall be recalled first:

net inputs to layer j

$$= [1 \quad -1 \quad 1 \quad 1 \quad 1 \quad 1 \quad -1 \quad 1 \quad -1 \quad 1 \quad 1 \quad 1 \quad 1 \quad -1 \quad 1]$$

$$\times \begin{bmatrix} -1 & 3 & -1 \\ 1 & -3 & 1 \\ 1 & 1 & -3 \\ 1 & 1 & -3 \\ -3 & 1 & 1 \\ -3 & 1 & 1 \\ 1 & -3 & 1 \\ -3 & 1 & 1 \\ 1 & -3 & 1 \\ -3 & 1 & 1 \\ -1 & 3 & -1 \\ -1 & 3 & -1 \\ -1 & 3 & -1 \\ 1 & 1 & 1 \\ -3 & 1 & 1 \end{bmatrix}$$

$$= [-21 \quad 27 \quad -9]$$

Taking the threshold gives $[-1 \ 1 \ -1]$, which is the associated pattern.
The pattern $[-1 \ 1 \ -1]$ can be used as the cue:

net inputs to layer $j = [-1 \quad 1 \quad -1]$

$$\times \begin{bmatrix} -1 & 3 & -1 \\ 1 & -3 & 1 \\ 1 & 1 & -3 \\ 1 & 1 & -3 \\ -3 & 1 & 1 \\ -3 & 1 & 1 \\ 1 & -3 & 1 \\ -3 & 1 & 1 \\ 1 & -3 & 1 \\ -3 & 1 & 1 \\ -1 & 3 & -1 \\ -1 & 3 & -1 \\ -1 & 3 & -1 \\ 1 & 1 & 1 \\ -3 & 1 & 1 \end{bmatrix}^T = \begin{bmatrix} 5 \\ -5 \\ 3 \\ 3 \\ 3 \\ 3 \\ -5 \\ 3 \\ -5 \\ 3 \\ 5 \\ 5 \\ 5 \\ -1 \\ 3 \end{bmatrix}^T$$

The original image pattern is obtained once the vector is passed through the activation function.

If the same process is repeated for the other vectors then it will be seen that all associations are recalled.

4.4 Autoassociative backpropagation

The standard feedforward backpropagation network introduced in Chapter 2 can be trained in an autoassociative way to perform tasks such as image compression. The technique is to make the target pattern the same as the training pattern so that the network learns to reproduce on the output layer that which is presented to the input layer. Figure 4.6 explains the basic architecture. The network is trained in the standard way except that the task is to associate each training pattern with itself. Upon successful completion of training, the network can act as two machines: the first layer of weights can serve to compress a pattern and the second layer of weights can serve to reconstruct the full pattern from its compressed representation. Of course, some loss in reconstruction is to be expected because the network will not re-create perfectly all training instances on the output layer. A pattern is compressed by presenting it to the input layer and propagating signals to calculate the activations for each hidden unit. For a network with a 20-10-20 architecture (20 input units, 10 hidden units and 20 output units), the compression ratio will be 2–1 because the hidden activations give the compressed vector for the input vector. To reconstruct the input vector, the compressed vector is presented to the hidden layer and activations are propagated to the output layer.

It may sometimes be useful to apply an autoassociative network to data before processing with another network model (even for another feed-forward network to perform classification). It is known, for example, that a single

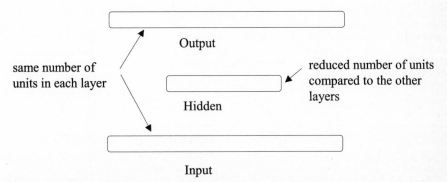

Figure 4.6 An autoassociative feedforward network.

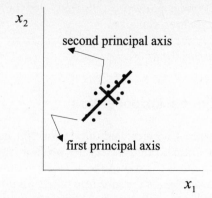

Figure 4.7 PCA can be used to represent data by deriving a new set of principal axes.

hidden layer feedforward autoassociative network computes what is essentially the principal components. Principal component analysis (PCA) is a standard statistical technique that is used to remove redundancy from data and to perform clustering. PCA also decorrelates the vector features (a feature corresponds to an element position) which might sometimes help in training another feedforward network. The idea is to transform the training data into a reduced description, with each hidden unit being a component of the reduced description.

PCA can be used to perform a lossy compression. For example, Figure 4.7 shows a cloud of two-dimensional data. A new pair of axes has been drawn through the data, with each axis at right angles to the other. These data points

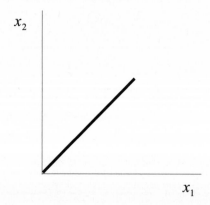

Figure 4.8 This straight line is plotted using a set of two coordinate values but can be represented by a set of single (one-dimensional) values.

Table 4.3 *Some sample points for the line $x_2 = x_1$ have been mapped to a single coordinate value*

x_1	x_2	Single coordinate value
1	1	1.414
3	3	4.243
4	4	5.657
8	8	11.314

can now be given coordinates in terms of these new 'principal axes'. The longest axis gives the direction of most spread or variance of the data. If the variance in the direction of the longest principal axis is 85% of the spread of the data and that on the second axis is 15%, then 85% of the variance of the data will be retained if the second principal coordinate is dropped. In other words, if each data point is described in terms of the longest principal component then most of the information about the data is retained but some information will be lost. Sometimes there is redundancy in the data, as illustrated in Figure 4.8. Data points sit on the straight line $x_2 = x_1$. Each data point can be described by a single 'principal coordinate' with no loss of information. So if the data are mapped onto the principal coordinate then each pattern is described by a single number instead of two. At first, this idea that patterns can be described by a single coordinate instead of two (only if there is redundancy, remember!) may appear strange. Consider, then, Table 4.3, which describes a number of two-dimensional points as a single coordinate. The transformation of the two-dimensional patterns to a single dimension is achieved as follows:

$$
\begin{bmatrix} 1 & 1 \\ 3 & 3 \\ 4 & 4 \\ 8 & 8 \end{bmatrix} \begin{bmatrix} \dfrac{1}{\sqrt{2}} \\ \dfrac{1}{\sqrt{2}} \end{bmatrix} = [1.414 \quad 4.243 \quad 5.657 \quad 11.314].
$$

The inverse mapping for 1.414 is given by:

$$
[1.414] \begin{bmatrix} \dfrac{1}{\sqrt{2}} & \dfrac{1}{\sqrt{2}} \end{bmatrix} = [1 \quad 1].
$$

The other coordinates can be reconstructed in the same manner.

A higher form of compression may sometimes be achieved by introducing additional hidden layers. For example, a network architecture of 40-20-8-20-40 could provide a compression ratio of 40 to 8, provided, of course, it trains successfully.

4.5 Summary

An associative network acts like a memory:

- Autoassociation relates a pattern to itself. For example, an autoassociative memory can be used to recover a clean version of a stored pattern given a noisy version of that pattern.
- Heteroassociation is a relationship between two different patterns. One pattern can be used as a cue to retrieve the other pattern from memory.
- Where autoassociatve learning is achieved by forcing signals through a narrow channel like the hidden layer of an autoassociative feedforward network, then a form of data compression is achieved. The compression can act as a useful form of pre-processing data before training with another network architecture.
- The Hopfield network can be used for autoassociation and bidirectional associative memory for heteroassociation.
- The weights for discrete Hopfield network and bidirectional associative memory can be found using simple matrix operations, and so there is no need for lengthy training.
- The number of units in an associative network has an effect on the number of patterns that can be stored.

4.6 Further reading

Haykin (1994) gives detailed coverage of the Hopfield Network and the autoassociative backpropagation network.

4.7 Exercises

1 Define the weights of a Hopfield network to store the pattern $[1\ 1\ 1\ -1]$.
2 Cue the network in Question 1 with the pattern $[1\ 1\ 1\ -1]$ to test whether it stabilizes on the stored pattern.
3 Repeat Exercise 2 for the pattern $[-1\ -1\ 1\ -1]$.
4 How many patterns would you expect to recall successfully from a Hopfield network if each stored vector has 10 elements?
5 (a) Define the weights of a Hopfield network to store the patterns

$$[-1\ \ 1\ \ -1\ \ -1\ \ 1\ \ -1\ \ -1\ \ -1]$$
$$[-1\ \ -1\ \ 1\ \ -1\ \ -1\ \ -1\ \ 1\ \ -1]$$

(b) Test the stability of the network when cued with the stored patterns.

(c) Test the stability of the network when cued with the patterns

$$[-1 \quad 1 \quad -1 \quad -1 \quad 1 \quad -1 \quad -1 \quad 1]$$

$$[-1 \quad 1 \quad 1 \quad -1 \quad 1 \quad -1 \quad -1 \quad -1]$$

6 Define the weights of a Hopfield network to store the patterns

$$[-1 \quad 1 \quad -1 \quad -1 \quad 1 \quad -1 \quad -1 \quad -1]$$

$$[-1 \quad -1 \quad 1 \quad -1 \quad -1 \quad -1 \quad 1 \quad -1]$$

$$[1 \quad -1 \quad -1 \quad 1 \quad -1 \quad 1 \quad -1 \quad -1]$$

Test the stability of the network when cued with the first stored pattern.

7 Define a BAM for Example 4.4, but this time take the following vectors as the associated patterns for each image:

Pattern	Associated pattern	
1	−1	1
2	1	−1
3	1	1

Discuss how the results compare with Example 4.4.

CHAPTER 5

A sample of recurrent networks

Aim: To introduce networks with recurrent connections.

Objectives: You should be able to:

describe why recurrent networks are useful, and their advantage over non-recurrent networks for certain classes of problem;

describe a non-recurrent network architecture whose performance is equivalent to that of a recurrent network for the specific task;

to modify the backpropagation algorithm to implement a simple recurrent network.

Prerequisites: Chapters 1 and 2.

5.1 Introduction

In this chapter we take a brief look at some architectures that are designed to process sequences. A *sequence* is a succession of patterns that relate to the same object. For example, a sequence might be letters that make up a word or the words that make up a sentence. Sequences pose a challenge because they can vary in length. For example, the number of words that make up sentences can vary quite widely. If training patterns are allowed to have a varying number of elements, then how many inputs should there be? One way to handle a sentence with a fixed number of input units is to use a sliding window, as shown in Figure 5.1. The disadvantage with this approach is that a sequence has to be segmented and any dependence between distant words in the sequence is lost. To process the whole sentence in one go requires a neural architecture of a size that is capable of handling the longest anticipated sentence. A way round this problem is to use a network with recurrent connections.

5.2 Backpropagation through time

The backpropagation network introduced in Chapter 2 is a feedforward network, which means that all connections are constrained to go in one direction

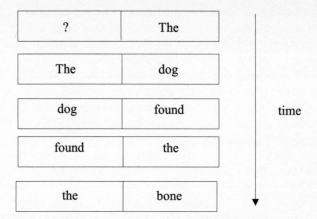

Figure 5.1 A sentence, 'The dog found the bone', is presented to the input layer of a network. The input layer has two fields of units to take two words at any point in time. The network takes four presentations of two words (current plus previous) before the last word, 'bone', is seen.

from the input layer towards the output layer. A backpropagation network need not be strictly feedforward, and can have recurrent connections so that a unit can feed activation back to itself, or to other units in the same or lower levels. In fact any combination of feedback is permitted. The feedback with a recurrent connection is not to be confused with the feedback of errors when adapting weights. The feedback of errors is a procedural part of adapting the weights, whereas a recurrent connection feeds back activation that will affect the output from the network during subsequent iterations.

The method of processing with a recurrent backpropagation network is a relatively straightforward extension of the feedforward case. This extension relies on the observation that for every recurrent network there is a feedforward network with identical behaviour. Figure 5.2 shows a network with connections

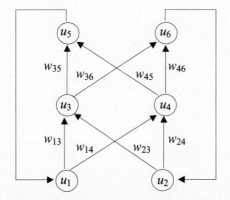

Figure 5.2 A recurrent backpropagation network.

feeding back from the output layer to the input layer, and Figure 5.3 shows this network processing for two time steps. Note that the additional feedforward layers have weights that duplicate the feedforward connections of the recurrent version: in other words, the network is duplicated to mimic the recurrent version for two time steps of processing.

During training a pattern is presented to the network and a feedforward pass is made. Each network copy corresponds to a time step and for each time step errors are calculated in the same way as for the standard backpropagation. The weight changes calculated for each network copy are summed before individual weights are adapted. The set of weights for each copy (or time step) always remain the same.

Rumelhart *et al.* (1986a) have performed a number of experiments with recurrent connections. One experiment involved training a network to perform sequence completion. A sequence consisted of six characters, with the first two being letters chosen from the set {A, B, C, D, E} and the remaining four being

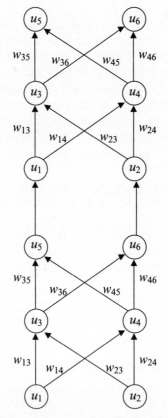

Figure 5.3 An expanded version of the network in Figure 5.2. The network is to process a

selected from the integer set $\{1, 2, 3\}$. The first two letters determined the rest of the sequence. For example, if 'A' denotes the sequence '12', and 'C' the sequence '13', then the complete sequence prefixed by 'AC' would be 'AC1213', and that by 'AA' would be 'AA1212'. The network consisted of five input units (one for each letter), three output units (one for each number) and 30 hidden units. Each hidden unit was connected to itself and every other hidden unit, and each output unit was connected to itself and every other output unit. Training to predict the completed sequence followed the steps below:

Time step 1. Put the activation of the input unit corresponding to the first letter to 1 and all other input units off.
Time step 2. Put the activation of the input unit corresponding to the second letter to 1 and all other input units off.
All input units are then switched off.
Time step 3. The target output is the third character (i.e., the first number).
Time step 4. The target output is the fourth character (i.e., the second number).
Time step 5. The target output is the fifth character (i.e., the third number).
Time step 6. The target output is the sixth character (i.e., the fourth number).

All hidden unit and output unit activations started at 0.2. The network was trained on 20 sequences. It was shown that the network could complete the sequences for five test cases when given the first two characters. Another experiment also demonstrated that sequences could be completed even when there were delays in presenting the first and second letter (for example, 'C *delay* A *delay* 1312').

EXAMPLE 5.1

A 3-2-2 fully connected feedforward network has recurrent connections where a hidden unit connects to itself and to every other hidden unit and an output unit connects to itself and to every other output unit. Sketch the network and its equivalent feedforward network with no recurrent connections, for a single time step. The single time step in this example means that an input pattern will have passed between two hidden units and two output units.

SOLUTION 5.1

The solution is sketched in Figures 5.4 and 5.5

Neural network models that place no restriction on the number and level of recurrent connections can appear somewhat intimidating when first met. The network discussed in the next section is easier to comprehend and requires only a simple modification to the standard backpropagation network. This network, the simple recurrent network, albeit a basic architecture, is widely used.

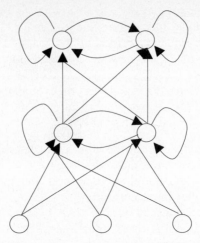

Figure 5.4 A network with full recurrent connections on the hidden and output layer.

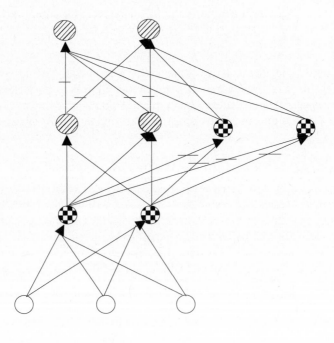

⊕ Hidden unit

⊘ Output unit

Figure 5.5 The weights that are crossed are the recurrent connections in Figure 5.4. The two sets of weights between the hidden and output units maintain the same values.

5.3 The simple recurrent network

Jordan (1989) introduced one of the early forms of recurrent network. The Jordan network has connections that feed back from the output to the input layer and some of the input layer units feed back to themselves. The architecture is shown in Figure 5.6. The network is capable of learning how to process tasks that are dependent on a sequence of successive states. The network can be trained using backpropagation.

The recurrent connections in the Jordan network allow the network's behaviour to be shaped by previous inputs. The network has a form of short-term memory. Another, and very popular recurrent network with a similar form of short-term memory is the *simple recurrent network* (SRN).

Elman (1990) has demonstrated that an SRN can predict the next item in a sequence from the current and preceding input. In an SRN the hidden units are

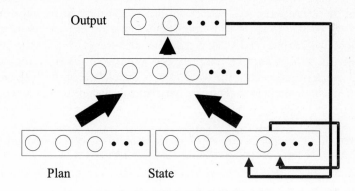

Figure 5.6 Jordan network.

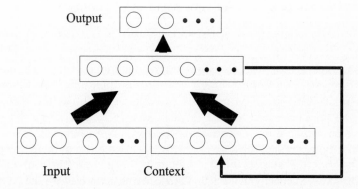

Figure 5.7 Simple recurrent network. The number of context units is the same as the number of hidden units.

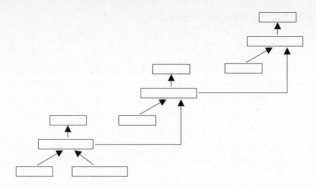

Figure 5.8 Expanded version of the SRN in Figure 5.7 over three time steps.

fed back into the input layer, as shown in Figure 5.7. An expanded version of an SRN for three time steps is shown in Figure 5.8. The hidden units represent an internal reduced representation of the data in the sequence that precedes the current input. This reduced representation provides context which is essential for certain tasks. For example, the third item in the sequence $\{110, 000, 101, 011\}$ cannot be uniquely predicted from the second or the first item independently. Instead, the third item is dependent on both the first and second items in the sequence. The first two items in each of these sequences correspond to the bit patterns of the XOR problem, and Elman has demonstrated that an SRN can learn the XOR.

For the XOR problem, an SRN is trained on a long sequence of bits. In this sequence, the first and second bits are XORed to give the third; the fourth and fifth are XORed to give the sixth, etc. The network had to learn to produce the next item in the sequence. An example input and output is given below:

$$\text{input:} \quad 1\ 0\ 1\ 0\ 0\ 0\ 0\ 1\ 1\ 1\ 1\ 0\ 1\ 0\ 1\ldots$$

$$\text{output:}\ 0\ 1\ 0\ 0\ 0\ 0\ 1\ 1\ 1\ 1\ 0\ 1\ 0\ 1\ ?\ldots$$

In one experiment, an SRN consisting of one input unit, two context units (and therefore, two hidden units) and one output unit was trained on a sequence of 3000 bits. The result of training showed that the network had learnt the temporal structure of the sequence in that at every third bit the squared error would drop. This drop in error is consistent with the temporal structure. For example, the network is always attempting to XOR the previous two bits, but the success of this will only be guaranteed every third bit. Consider the sequence: 1 0 1 1 1 0. The third and sixth bits are the XOR of the previous two bits and so the error will be low when predicting the third and sixth bits.

5.3.1 Applying the SRN

Learning a simple grammar

Cleeremans (1993) has performed a number of interesting experiments with SRNs. One task was to get an SRN to learn the Reber grammar given in Figure 5.9. The grammar is expressed as a finite-state machine. Using this machine, a string of characters can be generated that conforms to the grammar. Also, a check can be made to see if a string is grammatical.

To generate a string, start at the begin node, B, and take an arc that points to another node. Every time an arc is traversed note down its label (character). When the end node, E, is reached, there is nowhere else to go and the string terminates. For a string to be grammatical, it must be possible to generate that string by following the arcs in the machine. Example strings are:

B P V P X T V P X V V E
B P V P X V V E
B T X S E
B P V V E
B T S S X S E
B P T T T V V E

We have repeated one of Cleeremans experiments with some minor modifications. Remember, the idea is to get an SRN to learn the grammar. Six input units and six output units were used with a single unit representing a single character. The units for the input and output layers were arranged as shown in Figure 5.10. A program was created in order to generate randomly 20 000 strings that conformed to Reber's grammar (Cleeremans used 60 000). During training, a single character from a string was presented to the input

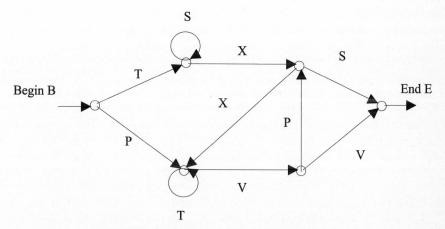

Figure 5.9 Finite-state machine for the Reber grammar.

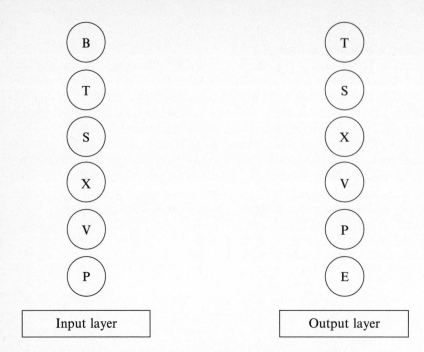

Figure 5.10 Unit representations for the input and output layers.

layer and the next character in the sequence was presented as the target output. The context units started at 0.5 for each sequence. After the first character had been propagated through the network, the second character was presented with the third as the target output. The hidden unit activations that were generated by the first character were copied to the context units before presenting the next input. The process was repeated for all characters in the sequence and the procedure repeated for each of the 20 000 patterns. The learning and momentum rates were set at 0.1 and the network was trained for three passes through all of the patterns. Weights were updated after each presentation of a character.

The results of training show that the network models the probability of one character following another. For instance, at each node in Reber's grammar one of two arcs can be taken with equal probability (the training strings were generated so that each path was equally likely to be taken). An interesting feature of the grammar is that each character is represented by two arcs and the legal succeeding state depends on which arc is being traversed. For example, the P that emerges from the start state can be followed by a T or V but the other P in the grammar can only be followed by an S or X. So a character like P can be followed by four different characters but only two will be legal at any point in the sequence.

Figure 5.11 shows the successive network state for all units when processing the sequence B P V P X V V. For each state, two output units will be strongly

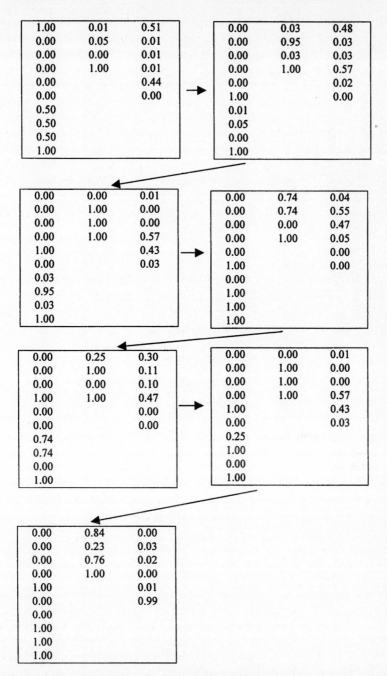

Figure 5.11 Network unit activations when processing BPVPXVV. The first six units of the input layer represent the characters and the next three are the context units. The last units in the input and hidden layers are bias units and so are always set to 1.

activated since there are two possible states that can follow. The first state, B, activates T and P on the output layer since both are legal successors and both occur with equal probability. The first P shows T and V as possible succeeding states but the second P shows X and S, as we would expect.

Cleeremans used his trained SRN to test whether it would accept 20 000 randomly generated strings that conformed to the grammar as grammatical. The network correctly accepted all of the 20 000 strings. The network was then tested on 130 000 strings that were generated randomly but not constrained to be grammatical. That is, a string was built by randomly selecting one of the five characters (T, S, X, V, P) as the next in the sequence. Of the 130 000 strings, 260 happened to be grammatical and the remainder (99.8%) non-grammatical. The network performed perfectly, rejecting non-grammatical strings whilst accepting grammatical ones. The network also performed correctly with extremely long strings (of the order of 100 characters).

Learning to add numbers

Next, we shall take a look at using an SRN for adding numbers. For simplicity, we shall concentrate on adding integer values. Assuming a representation of eight bits, the number 11 is binary 00001011, and the number 9 is binary 00001001. The addition in binary is given by:

$$00001011$$
$$00001001$$
$$\overline{00010100}$$

Addition in binary is similar to decimal addition. The digits are added in each column, working from right to left. If the sum is greater than 1, 0 is written and a 1 is carried to the next column. Only two digits are handled at a time and the combinations are

$$\begin{pmatrix} 1 & 1 & 0 & 0 \\ 1 & 0 & 1 & 0 \\ \overline{0} & \overline{0} & \overline{0} & \overline{0} \end{pmatrix}$$

where the bottom row is the sum of the two digits above. The result of the bottom row can be seen as the XOR of the two digits being summed. A carry of 1 will occur when the two digits to be summed are both 1. The AND of two bits is 1. So, the sum to be written can be executed with an XOR gate (*gate* is the name given to a hardware logic unit), and the carry with an AND gate, as shown in Figure 5.12. This circuit is known as a *half-adder*, and by complementing this circuit with a few more logic gates, full binary addition is possible. We know that a neural network can be trained to implement XOR, and the

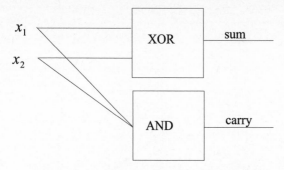

Figure 5.12 A logic circuit known as a half-adder.

AND circuit would be even more trivial to implement. It is possible, therefore, to devise a modular neural network to perform binary addition. Since logic gates form the basis of computation at the hardware level, we can create similar hardware out of neural network circuitry to mimic a conventional computer. There is little point, though, in simulating conventional hardware with neural networks so we shall look for an implementation that has been learnt.

When we perform the addition of long numbers, unless we are exceptionally gifted, we use a tool of paper and pen to record the results of interim stages. We start the sum from the rightmost column, record the sum of the first two digits and mark on paper any carry bit (Figure 5.13).

Noelle and Cottrell (1995) have implemented a neural network adder where there is no explicit marking of carry information from one column to the next. Instead, the carry information is retained in the internal state of the network. Noelle and Cottrell used two types of neural network model: the simple recurrent network and a Jordan network. We shall concentrate on the SRN, but the same procedure was used for the Jordan network. The basic architecture is illustrated in Figure 5.14.

The 'write' unit indicates when a result is to be written, the 'carry' when carry information is relevant, the 'next' when the next pair of digits is to be presented, and the 'done' when the summation is complete. The steps involved in adding 865 to 327 are shown in Table 5.1. In all experiments a radix of 4 was used (that is, a bit is carried if the sum of two digits is greater than or equal to 4). Each digit was represented by two units.

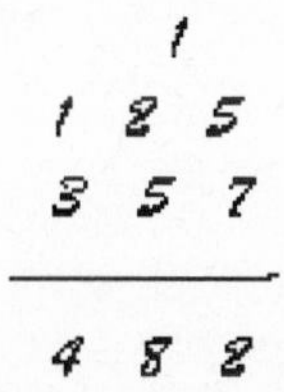

$$
\begin{array}{ccc}
 & 1 & \\
1 & 2 & 5 \\
3 & 5 & 7 \\
\hline
4 & 8 & 2 \\
\end{array}
$$

Figure 5.13 The addition of two numbers using pencil and paper.

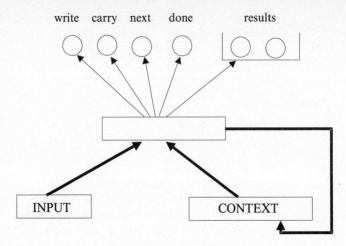

Figure 5.14 SRN for adding digits.

The training data consisted of numbers with no more than three digits. Initial training on small random subsets of the entire training corpus led to poor generalization: the network memorized the training data. A *combined subset training technique* (as dubbed by the authors) was used, where initially a small random subset of the training data is learned and then this subset is doubled in size until the entire training corpus can be represented. Results were impressive. The network could generalize to all training pairs after exposure to only 8% of the entire corpus. Furthermore, with some 'clean-up' training (exposure to a small subset of difficult training samples), the network could generalize to problems containing numbers with up to 14 digits.

Noelle and Cottrell discovered a difference in the performance of the Jordan network compared to the SRN. The Jordan network failed at the task when the order of output operations was changed slightly so that the announcement of

Table 5.1 *The sequence of steps for the SRN in Figure 5.14 to add 865 to 327*

Time step	1st digit	2nd digit	Write	Carry	Next	Done	Result
1	7	5	✓				2
2	7	5		✓			–
3	7	5			✓		–
4	2	6	✓				9
5	2	6			✓		
6	3	8	✓				1
7	3	8		✓			
8	3	8			✓		
9	0	0	✓				1
10	0	0				✓	

carry information was delayed until after the sum for the next column had been written. Both the Jordan network and the SRN are recurrent architectures but the SRN recirculates states that are derived as internal representations.

Through analyzing the states of the hidden units, Noelle and Cottrell showed that the SRN was acting as a kind of finite-state machine (a structure for simulating computational devices used earlier to represent a grammar). It is known that an SRN can be constructed to implement any finite-state machine (see Kremer, 1995). In principle then, the SRN should be useful for simulating many types of computing machine. The usefulness of the SRN is further highlighted with its application to a number of other tasks introduced in Chapter 8.

5.4 Summary

The networks introduced in this chapter require simple modifications of the backpropagation algorithm. These modifications enable recurrent processing:

- For every recurrent network there is a feedforward network with identical behaviour.
- Recurrent networks are used to process patterns that can have variable lengths. These variable-length patterns are treated as sequences; the sequence is split into chunks of data and each chunk is presented to the network at a different time step.
- Simple recurrent networks can demonstrate the ability to predict the next chunk of data in the sequence from the past history of data.

5.5 Further reading

Cleeremans' (1993) book on implicit learning provides a number of interesting examples using SRN's with some impressive results. Other examples using recurrent networks can be found in Chapter 8 of this text.

5.6 Exercises

1 An SRN has five input units, eight context units and four output units. How many weights does the network have?
2 An SRN has been trained on a set of variable-length character strings. The characters always appear in alphabetical order. For example:

B C D E end
B C D E F G end
E F G H end

The network has been trained to predict the next character in the sequence. Without any concern for the number of units, sketch the equivalent feedforward network for the SRN when processing the sequence E F G H end. Show the input and desired output at each stage.

3 How many input units would you use for Question 2? Give reasons for your choice.

4 An SRN is to be trained on sequences made up from eight characters plus NIL {B, R, A, E, T, N, S, I, NIL}. The order in which the characters appear in a sequence does not matter but each sequence must contain at least one vowel and one consonant and must end with NIL. The characters in a sequence are presented to the SRN in left to right order but the target output is always the complete sequence: the network is being trained so that it will attempt to predict the complete sequence from the characters it has seen so far.

(a) Devise a number of training instances.

(b) Propose a network architecture for the SRN and explain why you opted for this architecture.

CHAPTER 6

Some other network models and a few practical points

Aims: To introduce some other neural network models and to discuss some practical issues.

Objectives: You should be able to:

describe the principle of simulated annealing and how it is utilized in neural networks;
understand the basic probabilistic neural network sufficiently to be able to simulate it in a spreadsheet program;
explain in simple terms what the Boltzmann machine is;
discuss some of the practical issues that arise when using neural networks.

Prerequisites: Chapters 1–5. A very basic knowledge of statistics is assumed.

6.1 Introduction

The previous chapters have introduced what can be considered the essential models for a basic grounding in neural network technology. The aim of this chapter is to introduce a few other network models and some practical issues to be considered when using neural networks. The chapter starts with network models that emerge from statistical techniques. The emphasis of this section will be the probabilistic network; simulated annealing and the Boltzmann machine are really only introduced to make the reader aware of their existence. This section is followed by an example of a modular architecture constructed from models presented in previous chapters. The intention is to show how new models can be constructed and to give the reader some appreciation that solutions might exist for problems that can at first appear intractable.

6.2 Networks that use statistics

So far, all of the neural network models we have looked at use *deterministic* learning algorithms. By 'deterministic' we mean that when a unit's weights or a unit's activation are scheduled to be changed, we can determine by direct calculation the amount of change. Even in a Hopfield network, where the unit being updated is selected at random, the change is deterministic since once a unit is selected we can calculate with certainty its new activation. In contrast, with a *stochastic* learning algorithm we do not know at any point in time how a network's state will change (by 'state' we mean the current weight values and unit activations). In other words, we cannot predict the next state given the current state. For example, if we use a stochastic algorithm for updating a unit's state in a Hopfield network, a probability distribution function is used to determine whether or not the unit should change to the new calculated state. So, even when a unit is selected for updating, it might not be updated to a new state. Although we cannot say how a stochastic network will respond at any point in time, we do know, in general terms, how the network will behave after a long period of operation.

6.2.1 Simulated annealing

Simulated annealing is a technique that is often used to solve optimization problems. The solution to the problem being tackled is formatted in a way that requires a cost function to be minimized. The cost function is defined in terms of the global energy of the network. There is for example, a cost associated with each route that a salesman decides to take when visiting clients in different cities. The cost may be expressed in terms of distance travelled, in which case the cost function could return the distance for a selected route. Those routes with shorter distances have a lower cost. The most optimum route is a route with the shortest distance. Although we might not expect to find the most optimum solution, we would expect to find a reasonably optimal solution.

Simulated annealing is based on the analogy with the annealing of a metal. When a metal is annealed, it is heated almost to its melting point and then cooled slowly back to room temperature. The annealing process makes the metal more pliable so that it can be shaped without breaking. When the metal is heated to a high temperature the atoms move around in a violent random manner. If the metal is suddenly cooled, the atoms will be locked in random orientations. If, on the other hand, the metal is cooled slowly the atoms will tend to line up. The crucial part of the process is controlling how the temperature is cooled.

The analogy with function optimization can be seen with the aid of Figures 6.1 and 6.2. Figure 6.1 shows the curve of a hypothetical function of one variable. The function is not smooth and several minima can be observed. The procedure for finding the global minimum is simple. A range over which the function is to be evaluated is chosen. The function is evaluated at a number of randomly chosen points and the lowest point remembered. The range is

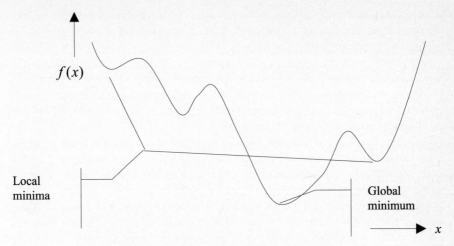

Figure 6.1 Illustration of local and global minima.

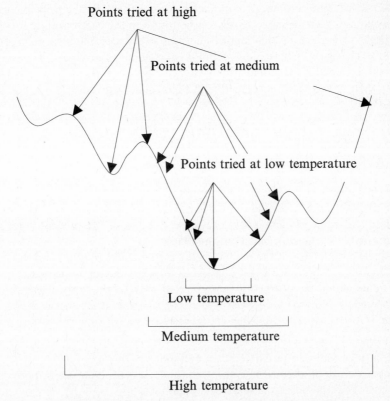

Figure 6.2 Finding a global minimum using simulated annealing.

then reduced and the function evaluated again at a number of random points. Again the lowest point is retained. The process repeats, with the range gradually reducing.

The selection of the range and its reduction is analogous to setting an initial high temperature and then reducing that temperature in stages. Initially, a point can wander around in a wild manner, hopping from one end of the curve to the other since the range is large. Again this is analogous to the wild motion of atoms in a metal at high temperature.

Another application for simulated annealing is to escape local minima. A deterministic algorithm like backpropagation that uses gradient descent, often gets caught in a local minima. Once caught, the network can no longer move along the error surface to a more optimal solution. Algorithms like gradient descent always attempt to move downhill to reduce the overall error, but sometimes it is necessary to make things worse before any further progress can be made. Simulated annealing enables a network's performance to worsen before improving. When, for example, a point on the curve is evaluated, that point is always accepted if there is an improvement but occasionally it will be accepted even if the new point makes things worse.

There is no definitive simulated annealing algorithm, but the principle upon which simulated annealing is based can be found in the Metropolis algorithm. The basic procedure of this algorithm is to select at random a part of the system to change (for example, a component element of a vector). The change is always accepted if the global system energy falls, but if there is an increase in energy then the change is accepted with probability p given by

$$p = \exp\left(-\frac{\Delta E}{T}\right) \tag{6.1}$$

where ΔE is the change in energy and T is temperature.

Example algorithm for function minimizing
We shall now look at a simple simulated annealing algorithm for the minimization of a real-valued function $f(\mathbf{x})$ of a binary vector $\mathbf{x}$. The procedure follows that presented by Geman and Hwang (1986).

A single component of the binary vector is selected at random and the bit is flipped (so that 0 becomes 1 and 1 becomes 0). The function is evaluated to see what value would be returned if the proposed change (the flipped bit) were to be accepted and the change in energy is also calculated. If the energy drops, the change is accepted, otherwise the change is accepted with the probablity given in equation (6.1). The procedure in detail is:

1 Select at random an initial vector $\mathbf{x}$ and an initial value of T.
2 Create a copy of $\mathbf{x}$ called $\mathbf{x}_{new}$ and randomly select a component of $\mathbf{x}_{new}$ to change. Flip the bit of the selected component.
3 Calculate the change in energy.

4 If the change in energy is less than 0 then $\mathbf{x} = \mathbf{x}_{new}$. Else select a random number between 0 and 1 using a uniform probability density function. If the random number is less than $\exp(-\Delta E/T)$ then $\mathbf{x} = \mathbf{x}_{new}$.
5 If there have been a specified number (M) of changes in $\mathbf{x}$ for which the value of f has dropped or there have been N changes in $\mathbf{x}$ since the last change in temperature, then set $T = \alpha T$.
6 If the minimum value of f has not decreased more than some specified constant in the last L iterations then stop, otherwise go back and repeat from step 2.

M is smaller than N, and L is usually much larger than N. The drop in temperature is goverened by α, a small constant typically between 0.8 and 0.9999. The initial value of T is chosen so that for all energy changes, $\exp(-\Delta E/T) \geq 0.9999$.

Boltzmann machine

The Boltzmann machine, introduced by Ackley *et al.* (1985), is a neural network that uses the idea of simulated annealing for updating the network's state. In its basic form, the Boltzmann machine is a Hopfield network (see Chapter 4) that uses a stochastic process for updating the state of a network unit. The presentation given here assumes bipolar activation states (+1 and −1). The energy of a Hopfield network was given in Chapter 4 as

$$E = -\frac{1}{2} \sum_j \sum_i s_j s_i w_{ij}$$

where s is the state of a network unit. Also if a unit j changes state by Δs_j then the change in energy is:

$$\Delta E = -\Delta s_j \sum_i s_i w_{ij}$$

The change in energy can also be expressed as:

$$\Delta E = -2s_j \sum_i s_i w_{ij}$$

This is easy to see by considering the possible change in the state of a unit. If the state of s_j is currently −1 and it changes to +1 the change is +2 or ($-2s_j$). If s_j is currently +1 and changes to −1 the change is −2 or ($-2s_j$). A sigmoid-shaped function is typically used for calculating the probability of accepting a proposed change in state:

$$p = \frac{1}{1 + \exp\left(-\dfrac{\Delta E}{T}\right)}$$

So, the probability of a unit changing to a new state is given by

$$p = \frac{1}{1 + \exp\left(2s_j \dfrac{\sum_i s_i w_{ij}}{T}\right)} \tag{6.2}$$

The Boltzmann machine has been applied to a number of optimization problems including the travelling salesman problem (finding an optimum route between a number of cities).

A Boltzmann machine can also be constructed with hidden units. The visible units (those used for interfacing to the environment) can be split into input and output units. An example architecture is shown in Figure 6.3. All the units have bidirectional connections to every other unit apart from those units in the input layer which do not connect directly to units in the output layer. With this architecture the network can be made to undergo supervised learning. During training the input and output units are clamped (set to input and associated target vectors). After training, only the input units are clamped and the network runs for a number of iterations until the activations of the output units become settled.

There are two phases of training for a supervised Boltzmann network: a clamped phase during which the input and output units are clamped to input and target patterns; and a free-running phase during which only the input units are clamped. Network statistics are gathered during both phases, which are then used to update the network's weights.

Input layer   Output layer

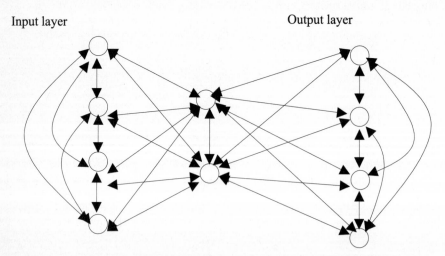

Figure 6.3 An example of a Boltzmann machine with input and output layers. In this case the network has the same number of input and output units and could be used for autoassociation.

The weight between units i and j are adjusted according to

$$\Delta w_{ij} = \eta(\rho_{ij}^+ - \rho_{ij}^-)$$

where ρ_{ij}^+ is the correlation between units i and j during the clamped phase and ρ_{ij}^- is the correlation during the free-running phase; for our purposes, correlation refers to the probability of any two units both being in the 'on' state. We shall not look in detail at the algorithm, but basically, for each input–output pattern, the visible units are clamped and simulated annealing performed. At each temperature, the network is relaxed by updating the states of the hidden units according to the probablity rule presented in equation (6.2). At the final temperature, statistics are gathered to estimate the correlations ρ_{ij}^+. The procedure is repeated for the free-running phase, following which the weights are updated. The whole process repeats until there are no changes in the weights (that is, the network has converged).

6.2.2 Probabilistic neural networks

In this section we introduce a network that can be used for pattern classification, the *probabilistic neural network* (PNN). A PNN is really a parallel implementation of an old statistical technique. It was Specht (1990) who showed how a neural network could be used to implement a statistical technique for performing pattern classification. Before looking at the details of the network architecture, we shall take a brief look at the concept of how these networks work.

In a PNN, a pattern is classified based on its proximity to neighbouring patterns. The distance from neighbouring patterns is an important factor in the classification of a new pattern, but the manner in which the neighbouring patterns are distributed is also important. Statistical methods use a number of techniques to decide on which class an unclassified pattern belongs to. Consider Figure 6.4. A simple metric to decide the class of a new sample is to calculate the centroid for each class (the location that is the average for all patterns in a class). This will work fine for distributions like those shown in Figure 6.4(a) but could lead to the wrong class assignment in Figure 6.4(b). An alternative, simple and often used metric is to base the classification on the nearest neighbour: you find which pattern, with a known class, is closest and assign the unknown pattern to the same class. Again this metric does not always work, as illustrated in Figure 6.4(c). A more sophisticated technique will examine the density of neighbouring patterns in addition to distance.

The PNN is based on Bayes's technique of classification. The idea is that, given a sample pattern, we can make a decision as to the most likely class that sample is taken from. The decision requires us to estimate a probability density function for each class. This estimate is constructed from the training data. The formulation of the rule means that the class with a highly dense population in

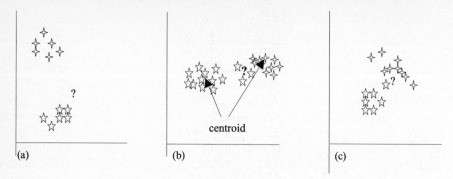

(a)   (b)   (c)

Figure 6.4 Techniques for the unsupervised classification of a point. In (a) it looks as though the unknown pattern, denoted '?', belongs to the ☆ class; in this case, the centroid method will give the correct class. In (b) it looks as though the unknown pattern belongs to the ☆ class; in this case, however, the centroid method will give the wrong class. In (c) it looks as though the unknown pattern belongs to the ✦ class. Its nearest neighbour is not really representative of the other samples belonging to the ☆ class. In this case, correct classification relies on the distribution of all neighbouring patterns.

the region of an unknown sample will be preferred over other classes. Also a class with a high prior probability or a high cost of misclassification will be the preferred choice. For two classes A and B the rule selects class A if

$$h_A c_A f_a(\mathbf{x}) > h_B c_B f_B(\mathbf{x})$$

where h is the prior probability, c is the cost of misclasification and $f(\mathbf{x})$ is the density function. The estimation of the cost of misclassification requires knowledge of the application, but for many applications the cost of misclassification and the prior probabilities are treated as the same for each class.

Ignoring the cost and prior probabilities still leaves us with the task of estimating the probability density function (PDF). The estimate can be found using Parzen's PDF estimator which uses a weight function that is centred at a training point. The weight function is called a *potential function* or *kernel*. A commonly used kernel is a *Gaussian* function. The shape of this function

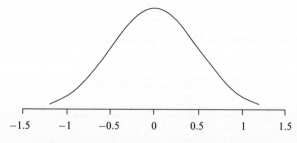

Figure 6.5 Gaussian function for a single variable.

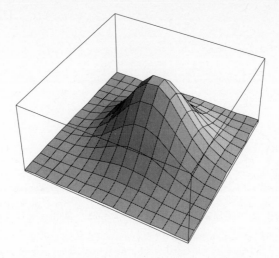

Figure 6.6 Gaussian function for two variables.

for a single variable is shown in Figure 6.5. For two variables (two dimensions) the function is bell-shaped, as shown in Figure 6.6. To estimate a PDF for a class, a Gaussian is centred at each training vector. The Gaussian functions for each vector are then summed to give the PDF. The estimated PDF for one-dimensional data belonging to a single class is illustrated in Figure 6.7. This time a more simplified form of Gaussian function is used, given by

$$g(\mathbf{x}) = \sum_{i=1}^{n} \exp\left(\frac{-\|\mathbf{x} - \mathbf{x}_i\|^2}{\sigma^2}\right)$$

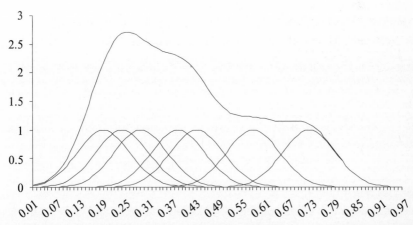

Figure 6.7 The estimated PDF is shown which is the summation of the individual Gaussians centred at each sample point. Here $\sigma = 0.1$.

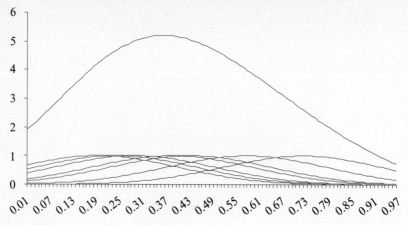

Figure 6.8 The same estimate as Figure 6.7 but with $\sigma = 0.3$. This width is too large, and there is a danger that classes will become blurred (a high chance of misclassifying).

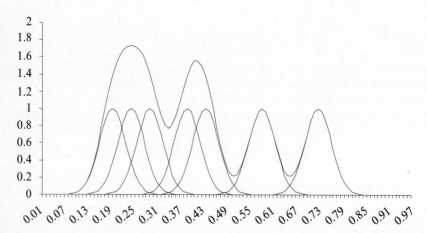

Figure 6.9 The same estimate as Figure 6.7 but with $\sigma = 0.05$. If the width becomes too small there is a danger of poor generalization: the fit around the training samples becomes too close.

The parameter σ controls the width of each function and its influence is illustrated in Figures 6.7–6.9.

EXAMPLE 6.1

There are two classes of data of a single variable, as shown in Figure 6.10. A sample positioned at 0.2 is from an unknown class. Using a PDF with a Gaussian kernel, estimate the class that the sample is from.

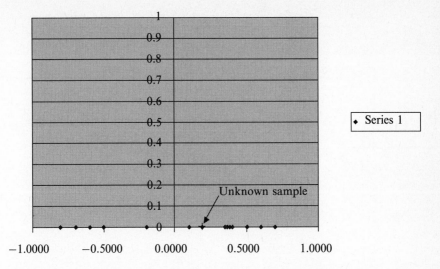

Figure 6.10 The unknown sample to be classified using a PDF (Example 6.1).

SOLUTION 6.1

The value for σ is taken as 0.1. Table 6.1 shows the result of the density estimation. Although the unknown sample is closest to a point in class A the calculation favours class B. The reason why B is preferred is the high density of points around 0.35.

The neural network architecture for a PNN

A sample architecture for a small problem is shown in Figure 6.11. The input layer's purpose is to distribute an input pattern to the pattern layer. In this case each input has four features. The pattern layer has a single unit for each pattern in the training data set. The input and the pattern layers are fully connected. The weights feeding into a pattern unit are set to the elements of the corresponding pattern vector. For instance, the first pattern unit will have its first incoming weight set to the first element of the first pattern vector, the second to the second element, etc. The activation of a pattern unit is

$$O_j = \exp\left(\frac{-\sum (w_{ij} - x_i)^2}{\sigma^2}\right) \qquad (6.3)$$

where $\mathbf{x}$ is an unknown input pattern. The above expression uses the squared Euclidean distance from an unknown sample to a pattern unit.

Table 6.1 *The calculation of the density estimation for Example 6.1*

Class	Training point	Distance from unknown	PDF
A	−0.2000	0.1600	0.0000
A	−0.5000	0.4900	0.0000
A	−0.6000	0.6400	0.0000
A	−0.7000	0.8100	0.0000
A	−0.8000	1.0000	0.0000
A	0.1000	0.0100	0.3679
			0.3679
B	0.3500	0.0225	0.1054
B	0.3600	0.0256	0.0773
B	0.3800	0.0324	0.0392
B	0.3650	0.0272	0.0657
B	0.3550	0.0240	0.0905
B	0.4000	0.0400	0.0183
B	0.5000	0.0900	0.0001
B	0.6000	0.1600	0.0000
B	0.7000	0.2500	0.0000
			0.3965

The summation layer has a unit for each class in the training set. A summation unit only has connections from those pattern units that belong to its class. The weights from the pattern to summation units are fixed at 1. A summation unit simply sums the outputs from the pattern units. This sum is the estimated density function value for the population of samples of the corresponding class. The ouput unit is a threshold discriminator which signals the summation unit with the maximum activation (that is, signals to which class an unknown sample belongs).

There is no training with a PNN in the sense of training a backpropagation network since all the PNN network parameters (number of units and weights) are determined directly from the training data.

The procedure for using a PNN is relatively straightforward. The network architecture is determined from the training data:

Number of input units = number of features

Number of pattern units = number of training samples

Number of summation units = number of classes

The first layer of weights is defined from the training patterns. The second layer is all set to unity. The weights in the final layer are set so that the output can act as a discriminator to signal the summation unit with the highest

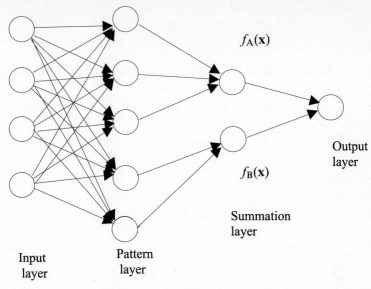

$f_A(\mathbf{x})$

Output
layer

$f_B(\mathbf{x})$

Summation
layer

Input
layer

Pattern
layer

Figure 6.11. An example PNN architecture.

activation. A choice has to be made for the pattern unit activation function. A typical choice is to use a Gaussian kernel of the type shown in equation (6.3). The value of σ controls the width of the activation function. The value of σ is critical and is often set by experimenting with different values to see which gives the best results.

Once the network is constructed an unknown pattern can be fed into the input layer and a forward pass through the network made, after which the most likely class to which the pattern belongs will be signalled at the output layer.

The presentation of the PNN given here requires that the Euclidean distance be calculated between the unknown sample and all training samples. If the input vectors are all of unit length, then the form of the activation function for a pattern unit can be modified to work with the more convenient sum of products:

$$O_j = \exp\left(\frac{\sum x_i w_{ij} - 1}{\sigma^2}\right)$$

EXAMPLE 6.2

Figure 6.12 shows a set of training points from three classes and an unknown sample. Normalize the inputs to unit length and, using a PNN, find the class to which the unknown sample is assigned.

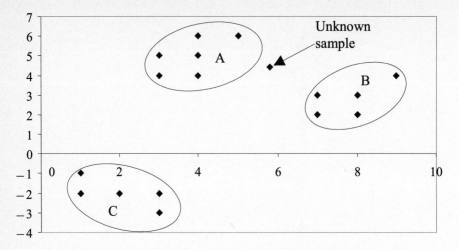

Figure 6.12 The unknown sample to be classified using a PNN (Example 6.2).

SOLUTION 6.2

The normalized vectors are shown in Figure 6.13. Table 6.2 lists the training data before and after normalizing. Table 6.3 gives the unknown pattern. Table 6.4 summarizes a pass through the network to classify the unknown pattern vector. The value of σ is 0.1. The calculations place the unknown pattern in class A.

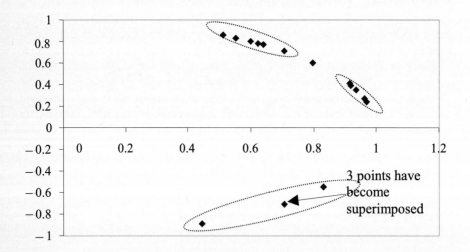

Figure 6.13 The vectors shown in Figure 6.12 are shown here after they have been normalized.

Table 6.2 *Training data normalized to unit length*

Unnormalized		Normalized	
x_1	x_2	x_1	x_2
3.0000	5.0000	0.5145	0.8575
4.0000	4.0000	0.7071	0.7071
3.0000	4.0000	0.6000	0.8000
5.0000	6.0000	0.6402	0.7682
4.0000	6.0000	0.5547	0.8321
4.0000	5.0000	0.6247	0.7809
7.0000	2.0000	0.9615	0.2747
7.0000	3.0000	0.9191	0.3939
8.0000	2.0000	0.9701	0.2425
8.0000	3.0000	0.9363	0.3511
9.0000	4.0000	0.9138	0.4061
1.0000	−1.0000	0.7071	−0.7071
1.0000	−2.0000	0.4472	−0.8944
2.0000	−2.0000	0.7071	−0.7071
3.0000	−2.0000	0.8321	−0.5547
3.0000	−3.0000	0.7071	−0.7071

PNNs can be made more complicated than presented here. For instance, a different value of σ could be used for each input feature. It is possible, therefore, to have considerable control over the shape of the classification surface that fits the training samples.

PNNs are useful classifiers. They are quick to train and they can tolerate erroneous data and provide useful results with small training sets. PNNs are expensive on resources. Some problems have hundreds or even thousands of training samples, which will result in a lot of processing time to classify an unknown sample. However, we must remember that if the network is implemented in hardware then most of the calculations can be performed in parallel.

The PNN is not as general as some other neural networks. For example, in its unmodified form it is limited to the task of classification, unlike a multi-layered feedforward backpropagation network which can also perform general function mappings. Nevertheless, classification is a widely used technique and classification is what PNNs do well. Indeed, Masters (1995) claims that the PNN is his favourite neural network.

Table 6.3 *Unknown sample*

Unnormalized		Normalized	
x_1	x_2	x_1	x_2
5.8000	4.4000	0.7967	0.6044

Table 6.4 *Computation of the PNN for classifying the unknown sample listed in Table 6.3*

Pattern unit	w_1	w_2	Activation	Activation of summed unit
1	0.5145	0.8575	0.0008	
2	0.7071	0.7071	0.3950	
3	0.6000	0.8000	0.0213	
4	0.6402	0.7682	0.0768	
5	0.5547	0.8321	0.0040	
6	0.6247	0.7809	0.0480	0.5459
7	0.9615	0.2747	0.0011	
8	0.9191	0.3939	0.0516	
9	0.9701	0.2425	0.0003	
10	0.9363	0.3511	0.0153	
11	0.9138	0.4061	0.0706	0.1389
12	0.7071	−0.7071	0.0000	
13	0.4472	−0.8944	0.0000	
14	0.7071	−0.7071	0.0000	
15	0.8321	−0.5547	0.0000	
16	0.7071	−0.7071	0.0000	0.0000

6.3 An example of a modular neural network

The BP-SOM network is a network that combines a multilayered feedforward network (MFN) trained with backpropagation and a self-organizing map (SOM). The motivation for introducing the BP-SOM is to show how, with a bit of inventiveness, new network architectures can be derived and to emphasize that neural networks should not be disregarded when at first they appear to fail at a task.

The architecture for a BP-SOM – see Weijters *et al.* (1997) for full details – is a standard feedforward network with one or more hidden layers. Associated with each hidden layer is an SOM. In the following description we shall assume a single hidden layer, but the use of more than one hidden layer follows the same procedure.

The number of SOM units is chosen arbitrarily and the number of inputs to each SOM unit is set to the number of units in the corresponding hidden layer. The MFN and SOM are trained in parallel. The activations of the hidden layer serve as inputs to the SOM. During training the SOM undergoes self-organization and this self-organization is translated into classification information by giving each SOM unit a class label. A SOM unit's class label is determined as follows. After a number of training cycles, all training patterns (along with their known output classes) are presented one after the other to the

MFN. The hidden layer activations for a training pattern are fed to the SOM and the winning SOM unit (the one whose Euclidean distance from the hidden layer activation vector is least) identified. Associated with each SOM unit is a counter for each of the output classes. Every time an SOM unit wins the competition for a training pattern its class counter corresponding to the pattern's class is incremented by one. After all training patterns have been presented, each SOM unit is labelled according to which class has the highest count. Along with a class label is a reliability value, which is a simple ratio of the class label count to the total number of times that unit has won a competition. An example architecture is shown in Figure 6.14.

There are two error vectors used to adapt the weights of the MFN during training. The first error vector is calculated using the standard backpropagation technique. That is, a pattern is presented to the MFN and the actual output compared with the desired output. The output error is then used to calculate an error value for each hidden unit ($v_{\text{bp\_error}}$). The second error is derived from the SOM. The hidden unit activations generated by the current input pattern are matched against the winning SOM unit that has the class label for the current pattern. In other words, the SOM units compete for the hidden activation vector but only those units with the correct class label take part in the competition. The difference between the hidden activation vector and the winning SOM unit's weight vector is taken to be the the SOM error ($v_{\text{som\_error}}$). If there is no SOM unit labelled with the current pattern's class, then $v_{\text{som\_error}}$ has all elements of its vector set to zero. The error for a hidden unit is then calculated according to:

$$v_{\text{bp\_som\_error}_j} = \begin{cases} ((1 - \alpha) \times v_{\text{bp\_error}_j}) + (r \times \alpha \times v_{\text{som\_error}_j}) & \text{if } r > t \\ v_{\text{bp\_error}_j} & \text{otherwise} \end{cases}$$

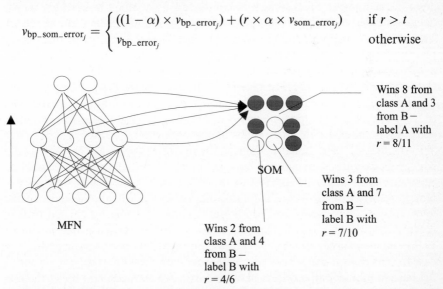

Figure 6.14 In this example, there are 27 training patterns, 13 from class A and 14 from class B. For purpose of illustration, only one SOM unit is shown with connections from the MFN.

where α denotes the influence of the SOM error and is typically set to 0.25 (if set to zero the result will be standard backpropagation), r is reliability and t is a threshold typically set to 0.95.

Training is the same as for a standard backpropagation network apart from the addition of an extra error term for each hidden unit:

1 Set the MFN and SOM weights to random values. For all SOM units, set the label to unknown and the class counters and reliability to zero.
2 Train the MFN for a fixed number of epochs (m). During each epcoh:
   (a) For each training pattern and associated output class: compute the hidden layer activation vectors for each pattern and use these vectors to train the SOM; calculate $v_{bp\_som\_error}$ and update the MFN weights.
   (b) After each nth cycle ($1 \leq n \leq m$) recompute the class labels and reliability of the SOM units.

Once trained, the MFN can operate in stand-alone mode.

An interesting feature of the BP-SOM is the claimed improvement in generalization. We know that good generalization is essential to any application because a network is of little use unless it can perform well with data it has not been presented with during training. It is quite common, for example, to find that an MFN trained with backpropagation learns a task with relative ease but fails to generalize to an acceptable level of performance. Sometimes simple measures improve poor generalization (for example, checking for overtraining), but often the solution is not that simple. When a network performs inadequately it is tempting to dismiss the network as being unsuited to a task. Clark (1993) describes a number of experiments conducted by various researchers whose networks failed to perform but later improved by changing the training set-up. The set-up is usually changed by decomposing the task. This might be done by phasing the presentation of training data (train on a sub-selection of the training data before introducing the remaining training instances) or by breaking the task into sub-tasks that can be tackled by separate networks.

One of the experiments reported by Clark is Norris's attempt (Norris 1989) to train an MFN to output the day of a week a given date falls. For example, given a date like 24 Februrary 1998 the network should output 'Tuesday'.

In the original experiment by Norris, the network was an MFN trained with backpropagation. Although the task could be learnt, the network failed to generalize even when the number of layers and number of units were varied. Norris resorted to analyzing a logical algorithm for calculating days of the week from a given date. The procedure for date calculation can be broken down into three steps. For example, a base month is chosen (say, November 1957) and each day for each date of the base month is specified. Secondly, any date for any month in the base year (1957) can be learned by applying offsets to the base month. Finally, offsets between years are learned (e.g., offset the day by one for consecutive years). Each step was modelled by a sub-network. The first sub-network completed training before training started in the second sub-network, and the second sub-network completed its training before the third. The generalization was about 90% accurate, with most failures falling on a leap year.

Although Norris eventually constructed a network with respectable performance, there was considerable human intervention. The solution relied on task-specific knowledge. While, in practice, real-world problems are solved using task-specific knowledge, it is important to discover how a neural network's performance can be improved. There are many occasions where neural networks are applied in a blind manner: we do not know how to solve some problem and so we try a neural network. Under these blind conditions, if the network fails we will not know if it failed because the task could not be learnt or because of the training set-up. Neural network practitioners accept that solutions to real-world problems usually require much experimentation, but all the time we are trying to make progress by developing new neural network models and by developing our understanding of how neural networks solve particular problems.

Weijters *et al.* (1997) solved the date task using a BP-SOM. The reported performance is impressive. They trained a standard MFN using backpropagation for comparison. In testing, the backpropagation network failed on 61% of test cases whereas the BP-SOM failed only on 3%.

In Chapter 8 we shall take a look at a few more modular architectures.

6.4 Some practical considerations for training neural networks

6.4.1 Choice of network model

The first decision to make when choosing a network model is the type of model, and this is dependent on whether or not the classification of training data is known. For example, training a system to recognize customers with poor credit rating is likely to involve supervised learning because a financial lender will have a record of whether a debt from a past customer has been paid. Sometimes there is no information as to the class into which data fall, and sometimes the classification is fuzzy. For instance, it is often difficult to give precisely the state of health of a machine such as a helicopter. Currently much effort is being devoted to monitoring the health condition of helicopters. On-board sensors log information which is later downloaded to a database on the ground for analysis. Assuming that a helicopter operates most of its time in a good state of health, the downloaded information can be analyzed to see if it varies significantly from previous flights. If there is something different in the data then it might be time to examine the aircraft more closely to see if a fault exists. Cluster analysis is often used in such situations. The Kohonen self-organizing feature map is an unsupervised neural network that has much in common with statistical clustering.

The nature of the problem, then, usually restricts the choice of network to one or two models. Sometimes, the final choice comes down to personal preference or familiarity. Other times the problem will once again restrict the choice. For instance, suppose a system is trained using a supervised technique with the network implemented in software, and, once trained, the task demands a fast execution time. The backpropagation network and the probabilistic neural network can both be used for supervised learning. If, however, the problem entails analyzing a very large data set with a large number of features the probabilistic network might become too restrictive for an operational system implemented in software. Consider, for example, a training set of 2000 patterns each with 30 features. The first layer of weights in the backpropagation network with 15 hidden units involves 30×15 multiply operations to process an unknown sample, whereas a probabilistic network will involve 30×2000.

6.4.2 Architecture

Aspects of a network architecture (such as the number of units) will often be determined by the problem. For instance, a probabilistic neural network will have an architecture that is more or less directly determined by the training data. A feedforward backpropagation network will have the number of input and output units dictated by the problem (number of input features and number of known classes). The size of the hidden layer is usually found by experimentation. A rule of thumb is to start with a single hidden layer that contains 30–50% of the number of units in the input layer. For a Kohonen self-organizing map, knowledge of the problem may give an initial idea for the number of network units. For example, although there may be no known relationship between the data set and its classification, it is usual to have some knowledge of how many classes of interest exist (for example, the types of fault that might occur with a machine). Usually there will be more than one unit per class to allow for classes that are split between different regions of the input pattern space.

6.4.3 Data

The availability and the integrity of data constitute the most important factor for training neural networks. The data should fully represent all possible states of the problem being tackled and there should be sufficient data to allow test and validation data sets to be extracted.

The data selected for training must be representative of the complete space a class might occupy. For instance, if two classes are located very close together, as shown in Figure 6.15, it is important to include data from the boundary that separates the classes to ensure that the network devotes resources to this region; otherwise samples from this region could be misclassified.

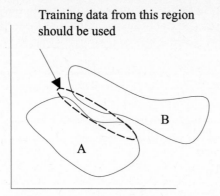

Training data from this region should be used

Figure 6.15 To classify unknown data successfully the network should be trained on representative data. To fit the boundary between classes A and B the network should be trained on sample points within the hatched region.

Data also need to be checked for consistency. It is common to find inconsistencies and errors in a large data set. It might be that an operator has entered information incorrectly or that some values for a pattern are missing. Sometimes outliers in the data exist. Outliers are points that stand out from the rest of the data and can indicate some form of error due to incorrect recording of the original data. Care has to be taken because sometimes outliers are representative of useful information (such as a machine fault). Even when supervised learning is to be used, it might be sensible to cluster the data first using an unsupervised technique or some other type of statistical analysis to identify any potential problems with the data. It might be possible to adjust problematic data or simply filter them out of the training set.

The test and validation sets should be selected at random and again they need to be representative of the problem. Validation data are often useful because test data are sometimes used to monitor network training (see Section 6.4.5).

Data will usually need scaling so that they lie within the operational range of the network. For example, the target data for a backpropagation network with sigmoid activation units need to lie between 0 and 1 because that is the range of the sigmoid function. Individual features might need to be scaled differently. Suppose one feature ranges from 300 to 2000 and another from 5 to 130 (say, height in millimetres and weight in kilograms). Then the first feature will tend to dominate the second since it has more influence on the input to a unit. A crude method of scaling is to divide each feature value by the maximum value for that feature. This limits the largest value to 1. It might be desirable to scale the data to lie within a certain range. For instance, the range 0.1 to 0.9 is often used for the sigmoid activation function to help prevent the network from grinding to a halt through running at the extreme limits of its operating range. A feature can be scaled into the range 0.1 to 0.9 using the following formula:

$$y = \frac{0.9 - 0.1}{x_{max} - x_{min}} x + \left(0.9 - \frac{0.9 - 0.1}{x_{max} - x_{min}} x_{max}\right)$$

where y is the new value and x is the original value. For example, suppose a feature ranges from 2 to 20. The value 2 becomes

$$y = \frac{0.9 - 0.1}{20 - 2} 2 + \left(0.9 - \frac{0.8}{20 - 2} 20\right) = 0.1$$

which is the new minimum value. The value 20 will be mapped to 0.9 and the value 5 to

$$y = \frac{0.9 - 0.1}{20 - 2} 5 + \left(0.9 - \frac{0.8}{20 - 2} 20\right) = 0.23$$

The values 0.9 and 0.1 could be changed to scale the data within an alternative range.

Different features might also have significantly different variation in the distribution of values. For instance, it might be that two features have a similar range and yet one of the features has most of its values at the maximum end of the range whereas the other has a more even distribution throughout the range. This is illustrated for 10 sample points in Figure 6.16. Another form of scaling

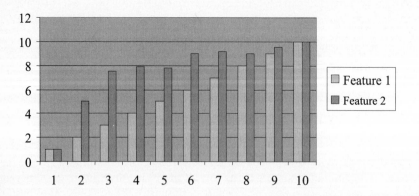

Figure 6.16 Two features with the same range but different distributions.

Table 6.5. *The data described by two variables, x and y, are transformed so that a single variable conveys the same information*

x	y	Transformed
1.0000	1.0000	1.4142
2.0000	2.0000	2.8284
3.0000	3.0000	4.2426
4.0000	4.0000	5.6569
5.0000	5.0000	7.0711
6.0000	6.0000	8.4853
7.0000	7.0000	9.8995
8.0000	8.0000	11.3137
9.0000	9.0000	12.7279

is to calculate the standard deviation and mean for each feature. Individual values are then scaled by subtracting the mean and dividing by the standard deviation for that feature.

For problems with many features, there will often be redundancy in the data. Redundancy means that it is possible to describe the data using fewer features and yet retain all of the information. This idea might seem strange, but the principle can be illustrated with a simple example. The x and y data in Table 6.5 are plotted in Figure 6.17. These data are convenient because they lie on a straight line. If now you imagine rotating the axis until the x-axis lies along the straight line, the x-axis can now be thought of as forming a new axis with all data points having 0 for their y component. In other

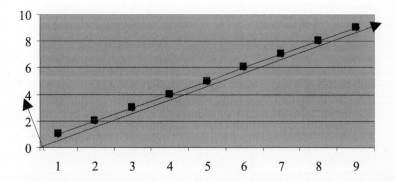

Figure 6.17 Straight-line plot of the (x, y) data in Table 6.15. If the data are represented by the new set of arrowed axes shown, then only a single coordinate is required.

words, we only need the new x axis to describe the data. The transformation can be performed by multiplying each x and y component by $1/\sqrt{2}$ and summing. Instead of describing the data with two features we now have only one. The transformation preserves the spatial relationship in the data. For example, the Euclidean distance between the point $(3, 3)$ and the point $(7, 7)$ is equal to the distance between the transformed points at 4.2426 and 9.8995 respectively.

Redundancy can be identified by means of principal component analysis (PCA). We introduced PCA in Chapter 4, but it is an important concept and so is presented again. PCA finds an alternative set of axes about which a data set can be represented. It also indicates along which axis there is most variation. For example, in the above illustration all the variance is along the new x-axis and there is zero variation along the new y-axis (hence it is not needed). After redundant information is taken out, it can sometimes be worth removing some of the minor components (it is usual to refer to a new axis as a component), which are those with very low variation. Some information will be lost if minor components are removed, but PCA will indicate how much information will be retained. You might, for example, decide to remove minor components but retain enough components to describe 95% of the data. In Figure 6.18, the two principal components have a different variation (or length). The first component is in the direction of most spread and the second has been placed at 90 degrees to the first. The second component describes the residual variation, which is the variation left after taking account of the first component.

An autoassociative backpropagation network performs a type of principal component analysis. For some problems, it might be useful to pre-process the data using an autoassociative network before tackling the problem using another network. The second network would take inputs from the hidden unit activations of the first network. You need to exercise caution when removing

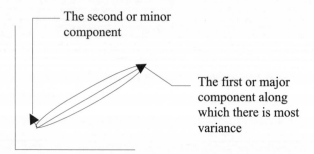

Figure 6.18 Data that are scattered within an elliptical shaped region can be represented by a new set of principal axes.

minor components because for some problems those minor components might contain information that is crucial to a solution.

Care must be taken not to introduce bias into the training set by the inappropriate representation of features. In the BP-SOM network described in Section 6.3, Weijters *et al.* (1997) used 12 input units to represent the months of the year. A different unit represented a different month. A naïve approach would have been to use a single unit and number the months 1 to 12. The numbering introduces bias since it is effectively saying that one month can have more influence than another month. In what sense is December more important than January for performing the data calculation?

6.4.4 Handling local minima

It is not uncommon for a backpropagation network to get stuck in local minima. A local minimum might be close to a solution but not close enough to satisfy the problem being tackled. Gradient descent works fine while the slope of the error function is heading downhill, but in practice the error surface for a large network will have many valleys, hills and folds. So, there will be plenty of places to get stuck.

The momentum term can help overcome the problem of local minima because the change in a weight includes a fraction of the previous weight change. If the previous weight change resulted in a large downhill shift in error, and the network is now in a local minimum, the previous weight change might help force the network to continue on the downhill slope since there is enough

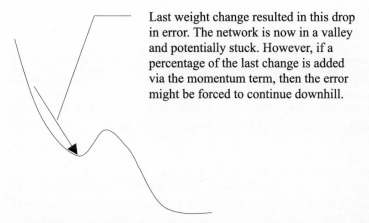

Last weight change resulted in this drop in error. The network is now in a valley and potentially stuck. However, if a percentage of the last change is added via the momentum term, then the error might be forced to continue downhill.

Figure 6.19 Attempting to avoid local minima by using momentum.

momentum to overcome the small valley. The idea of momentum is illustrated in Figure 6.19.

If a network looks as though it has become stuck, one easy solution is to scrap the current training run and start again with new random weights. For large networks, where many hours of effort have gone into training the network to a certain level of performance, it is disheartening to start again. Sometimes the location on the error surface can be shifted away from the local minimum by making a small random change to all of the network's weights. For instance, the minimum and maximum weight value could be found and a random percentage of this range (typically less than 10%) could be added to each weight.

An alternative technique to escape local minima in backpropagation networks is to use simulated annealing. Once the network becomes stuck, simulated annealing takes over to move back onto the downward slope of the error surface. Once back on the down slope, backpropagation takes over.

6.4.5 Generalization

A neural network is worth nothing if it cannot generalize. Generalization refers to how well a network performs with data it has not seen during training. With a backpropagation network, poor generalization can be due to having too many hidden units or overtraining.

Too many hidden units can be bad news for generalization. If the network has too many resources then it might memorize the training set. For example, consider an extreme case where the number of hidden units in a feedforward network matches the number of training patterns. With this quantity of resources, the network can memorize the training set by dedicating a single hidden unit to each pattern. Performance with unseen data is likely to be poor. It is sometimes possible to avoid memorization by continually changing the training patterns by adding up to 10% random noise (that is, a random fraction) to a pattern every time it is presented. The noise should be added to the original clean vector, otherwise in time the original training vector may no longer be representative of the problem being tackled.

Overtraining with too many hidden units means that the network fits the training data too well and there is not enough allowance for new samples that vary from the training samples. To prevent overtraining, training can be halted periodically and the test data passed through. If the overall error of the test set keeps dropping then training can continue. As soon as the error with the test set starts to increase, training should be stopped. Even if there are too many hidden units, it is sometimes possible to prevent overfitting by monitoring the training with the test set. If the test set is used for monitoring during training, there should be a validation data set which acts like another test except that it will not have been presented to the network in any form (that is, not for monitoring) during training.

6.5 Summary

There has been growing interest in the use of stochastic techniques. A number of network models employ the idea of simulated annealing for optimization tasks. Simulated annealing can also be used to assist gradient descent algorithms escape local minima.

The probabilistic neural network (PNN) in its basic form can be used for pattern classification:

- The PNN is a supervised model.
- Classification of an unknown pattern is based on the likelihood of that pattern being drawn from an existing class.
- The likelihood estimate is computed from the probability distribution of training samples.
- Training amounts to setting network parameters (weights) from the training instances and experimenting to adjust the probability estimates.

The availability and quality of training data crucially affect the performance of neural networks. Data often need to be pre-processed before presenting to a neural network. A neural network is worth nothing unless it generalizes to unknown instances.

6.6 Further reading

Most neural network books have some discussion on simulated annealing and the Boltzmann machine. Few cover the probabilistic neural network. Masters (1995) gives an in-depth but practical treatment of the probabilistic neural network. The reader needs a basic knowledge of C++ (or at least C) to appreciate Masters's book.

6.7 Exercises

1 Scale the following data listed below to the range 0.1 to 0.9:

$$-12, -8, -6, -2, 4, 8, 9, 15, 15$$

2 Repeat Question 1 for the range -0.9 to 0.9.

3 A large car-dealing chain wants to predict the type of car that a potential purchaser will opt for from features such as income, family status, etc. The car features will include performance and image. Discuss how you would encode features such as colour. Make a list of the features you think could be used for the task. From this list, make an estimate of the number of units that might be required for a feedforward network to perform the task and from the size of this network estimate the size of training set required. Justify your answers.

4 A PNN neural network is to be trained on the lower-case letters of the alphabet. The training data will cover six different fonts. If the characters are represented using an 11×11 pixel grid, give the number of units for the PNN.

5 Repeat Example 6.2 using $\sigma = 0.3$.

6 Repeat Example 6.2 using $\sigma = 0.5$.

7 Repeat Example 6.2, but this time use the unnormalized data and the Euclidean distance metric. Use $\sigma = 0.9$.

8 Repeat Question 7 using $\sigma = 1.5$.

9 Figure 6.20 shows three classes of data and an unknown sample point. The data are listed in Table 6.6. Calculate to which class the unknown pattern belongs using:
 (a) the nearest neighbour;
 (b) the centroid;
 (c) a PNN with $\sigma = 0.9$.

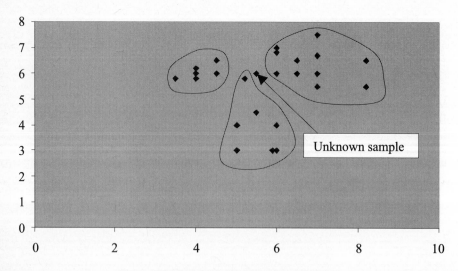

Figure 6.20 Plot of the data used for Question 9.

Table 6.6 *Data used in Question 9*

Class	x	y
Unknown	5.50	6.00
A	4.00	6.20
A	3.50	5.80
A	4.00	6.00
A	4.00	5.80
A	4.50	6.00
A	4.50	6.50
B	6.00	6.00
B	7.00	6.70
B	6.00	7.00
B	7.00	7.50
B	6.00	6.80
B	6.50	6.00
B	6.50	6.50
B	7.00	5.50
B	7.00	6.00
B	8.20	6.50
B	8.20	5.50
C	5.20	5.80
C	5.00	4.00
C	5.50	4.50
C	6.00	4.00
C	5.00	3.00
C	5.90	3.00
C	5.00	3.00
C	6.00	3.00

10 Repeat the PNN classification of Question 9 using $\sigma = 0.8$.
11 Repeat the PNN classification of Question 9 using $\sigma = 0.5$.

CHAPTER 7

Links to artificial intelligence

Aims:	To provide a very basic introduction to the symbol paradigm of artificial intelligence and the link to neural networks.
Objectives:	You should be able to:
	state the aims of artificial intelligence; state the essential ingredients of an intelligent system; give an outline description of symbolic reasoning; describe some of the difficult issues for natural language understanding systems.
Prerequisite:	General knowledge of computing.

7.1 Introduction

Neural networks can be applied to a whole range of engineering problems, and we have seen a few examples in the previous chapters. The neural architectures of these artificial nets are nothing like the human brain in terms of complexity and size, but they do constitute abstract *models* of the brain, and so the question arises whether artificial nets can provide 'artificial intelligence' (AI). AI is a major discipline within computer science with strong links to mathematics, psychology, philosophy and even neuroscience. It was recognized as a discipline in its own right during the 1950s, and since that time there has been a huge investment of time and money in researching the production of intelligent machines. The aim of AI researchers can broadly be described as building machines to perform tasks which humans do well but are not easily programmed using conventional computing approaches. The tasks that we do well but prove difficult to program often appear to us as mundane. For example, walking across a room or holding a conversation does not require the same conscious effort as adding up a list of numbers. The production of machines to perform such tasks is an enormous challenge to engineers. The fact that a machine can be built with relative ease to pass an undergraduate mathematics exam but not to vacuum-clean a house offers a challenge to our traditional notions of what it is to be intelligent.

The major part of AI research has concentrated on what is known as the *symbol paradigm* and is often referred to as 'traditional AI' or 'classical AI' (and sometimes GOFAI – good old fashioned AI). There is now a new form of AI based on connectionist nets (that is, neural networks) and evolutionary models (systems that are situated in an environment and adapt under the rule of the *survival of the fittest*). The new AI has not swept traditional AI to one side, and some believe it never will. Indeed, we may need a radical rethink to achieve truly intelligent machines. It can be argued that new AI is just a reimplementation of traditional AI, the argument justified on the basis that we still use the same computing devices at the lowest level (symbolic systems execute on a serial machine, and so do the majority of connectionist simulations). AI has yet to deliver what was promised in the early years, but we should still be buoyant about the importance of AI. After all, our demand for labour-saving devices is ever growing and so the desire for more intelligence is always implicit in any form of engineering. Certainly we will see the development of machines with increasing levels of intelligence but we will have to keep an open mind as to when it will be possible to build a conversational android. Even when such an android is built, philosophers will still debate whether or not the android possesses a conscious intelligence on a par with our own.

To move a new AI forward we need to understand something of traditional AI and perhaps bring both paradigms together under a general AI. In this chapter we will briefly look first at the nature of intelligence and then at traditional AI, before turning to connectionist developments in the next chapter.

7.2 The nature of intelligence

Intelligence is a concept that defies a concise definition. There are many components that contribute to human intelligence such as an ability to learn, sensory apparatus (for example, sight and touch) to interact with the environment, and an amount of knowledge that cannot be estimated. Even our pets may be considered intelligent: they have complex processing systems that enable them to recognize people, and they perform well at tasks requiring a great deal of skill.

Intelligent behaviour does not emerge from a central processor operating in isolation – the central processor (the human brain) relies on additional apparatus to sense, pre-process and structure data that it is fed. Intelligent agents can be built to operate in a completely virtual world, but these agents still need to perceive and develop desires and goals to behave intelligently. Research usually concentrates on some small aspect of intelligence and for practical reasons sensing channels and pre-processes are often substituted for by assuming appropriate structuring of data. Traditional AI would have us believe that it is theoretically possible (but not yet practically possible) to construct a mind – the ultimate embodiment of artificial intelligence – out of a computer; discover the right algorithm and a mind is there to be had. Within traditional AI the study of intelligent systems has centred around a few key topics: the representation of data, the ability to reason, and the ability of a system to adapt in an automated way (in other words, learn).

7.2.1 Knowledge and representation

An intelligent system embodies knowledge. When we talk of knowledge it may be the factual type of knowledge needed to take part in a quiz show, it may be the procedural type of knowledge applied in changing a car wheel, it could be knowledge observed as a skill such as riding a bicycle, or it could be the millions of bits of information we take as common sense such as not letting go of a cup while drinking. The representation of knowledge can be explicit or implicit.

Explicit knowledge can be stated and inspected: for example, in the form of facts

> An apple is a fruit.
> A cat is an animal.

or rules

> *If* the battery is flat *then* the car will not start.
> *If* interest rates rise *then* the cost of borrowing goes up.

Implicit knowledge is not easy to communicate. For example, a child can be given some general guidelines on riding a bicycle such as rotating the pedals and pointing the front wheel in the direction of travel, but a procedure cannot be written down which the child can read and then recall to ride the bicycle successfully. Instead, the knowledge of how to ride a bicycle is gained through an experience of trial and error.

Traditional AI is crafted out of symbolic processing, and knowledge is represented using symbol structures. The representation of knowledge comes in a number of forms and at different levels. Example representations are: knowledge expressed as rules; a child's rate of growth expressed as a graph; and the London Underground network shown as a map. The level of representation depends upon the level of detailed information that needs to be conveyed. For example, the London Underground map is an abstract view of the true network of connected stations. For the purpose of planning a journey between stations the map is sufficient since it shows all connections and station proximities. The lines connecting stations do not show the true curves in the rail tracks as this information is irrelevant and would confuse the visual appearance.

AI researchers look to knowledge of the brain for guidance on how to build artificial intelligence but it is difficult to formalize a theory of how humans

represent knowledge. Do humans categorize book-ends as stationery, ornaments or items of furniture? How can love be represented if a machine cannot
experience such emotion? Can a machine be made to experience love, and if it
can then will its understanding of love be different to ours? There are cognitive
theories of how knowledge is represented in the brain and these theories serve
as the basis for symbol representations.

7.2.2 Reasoning

Humans are adept at handling novel situations because they can deduce new
knowledge from existing knowledge and can make rational decisions based on
past experience and by thinking ahead about the possible consequences of those
decisions. The symbol paradigm attempts to mimic some of this behaviour with
programs that encapsulate a set of rules to perform case specific inferencing:

Rule: *If* the battery is flat *then* the car will not start.
Case-specific data: Susan's car has a flat battery.
New knowledge inferred: Susan's car will not start.

It is not difficult to program a system to perform basic rule inferencing, but
there are major issues to be addressed before a machine can possess any
modicum of real intelligence. The rules embody knowledge and the issues are
knowledge-related. What rules are needed and are sufficient to perform a task
intelligently? Consider a domain task restricted to knowledge of cars. An expert
system (a knowledge-based system equipped to perform inferencing within a
limited domain) enters into a dialogue:

Customer: Why do we have handbrakes on cars?
Expert system: To stop the car moving.

Customer: A car will not always move if the handbrake is off?
Expert system: Depends if you are on level ground.

Customer: What provides the power for the wheels to rotate?
Expert system: The engine.

Customer: So if the engine is running the wheels will rotate?
Expert system: If the clutch is engaged.

Customer: What happens if the engine is running with the handbrake on and
            then the clutch is engaged?
Expert system: You are supposed to release the handbrake first.

Customer: Yes, but suppose I don't.
Expert system: ???

A don't know response to the last question is reasonable if you are not an expert on cars but ridiculous if you are supposed to be. Someone who has never driven a car but has good knowledge about the physics of brakes and other mechanical devices might be able to reason a sensible answer. But knowledge of physics takes the expert system beyond the restricted domain of cars into a need for a broader level of knowledge. It is a problem for the system designer of such an expert system to know how much knowledge is required to perform adequately: it is difficult enough to validate a computer program that has a restricted form of input but the validation is much harder when the potential input cannot be foreseen during design. There are in existence impressive expert systems that act as labour-saving devices and are reported to save companies enormous sums of money. But demand too much from an expert system and it will soon appear brittle, because its knowledge is limited.

Other difficulties arise for people building expert systems. Consider a statement like the following:

> The experience was terrifying, I am lucky to be alive, all the men on the aircraft were killed.

Is the speaker a woman? Was she on the aircraft?

> I'm sure they will blame it on a woman pilot.

It seems reasonable to assume now that the speaker is a woman pilot and happened to be the only woman on board the plane that crashed.

> We collided on the approach to the airfield. Being in a single-seater jet I had an ejector seat.

The last piece of information causes us to revise earlier conclusions. Building an intelligent agent that makes a series of deductions but modifies those deductions at a later stage is just one of the many challenges facing developers of intelligent systems.

7.2.3 Learning

The survival of any animal is dependent upon an ability to adapt its behaviour based upon experience. We rely on our pets being able to learn so that we can train them to behave in a manner that is sociably acceptable.

Most computers are programmed to perform a task. A software engineer translates some problem description into an algorithm and then implements that algorithm using some high-level programming language. The communication of the problem and its implementation rely on knowledge and representation. For example, the area of a circle is easy to state as being equal to πr^2 where π is a numerical constant and r is the radius. Understanding the description relies on knowing that the radius is the length of a line connecting the centre of a circle to a point on the circumference, what the circumference is, and so on. The above formula expresses knowledge, but knowledge is also required about how to use the formula: the user needs to be aware that the area will be expressed in units which are the square of those used to measure the radius.

An example program for the formula in the C language is:

```
float areaOfCircle(float radius)
{
      float pi = 3.1415927;
      return (pi*radius*radius);
}
```

Internally the computer encodes π in a binary format, but this is of no concern to the programmer, just as the C implementation is of no concern to the program user, because understanding the algorithm depends only on a knowledge of everyday English and a few mathematical concepts.

The key to programming is being able to express the problem as an algorithm and to define a suitable representation. But what about knowledge that cannot be expressed explicitly? An inability to express a solution explicitly means that a program cannot be constructed in a traditional way. However, it may be possible to generate the program automatically via a process of learning. Machines can be programmed in much the same way as a dog learns a command. A command serves as input, a correct response is rewarded and the signal is repeated until the dog's behaviour adapts to a consistent response.

There are many symbolic learning algorithms but there is not the space to consider these in this chapter. The interested reader is referred to the further reading in Section 7.8.

7.3 The symbol system hypothesis

Traditional AI is based around the symbol system hypothesis. This hypothesis, in a much simplified version, states that, given a vast interconnected structure of symbols that represent knowledge of the world and a complex suite of symbol processes to operate on these structures to create new structures, a machine can be made to perform as a human. In a nutshell, the hypothesis says it is possible for computers to be programmed to think.

In this section we shall take a look at a couple of toy problems in order to get a handle on what symbol processing is about. We are not concerned here whether the hypothesis is believable, we simply need to get a feel for what is meant by symbol processes. We should also keep in mind that if a thinking machine can be built on the basis of this hypothesis, such a machine will embody a huge amount of knowledge coupled to a vast array of complicated processes. In this chapter we are stripping away complication to look at the nature of the computations. For pragmatic reasons, nearly all AI experimentation has been on a small scale, but if a human-like machine is possible things need to be scaled up dramatically. Well, a move in this direction has started (see Section 7.8).

7.3.1 Search

The solving of puzzles, the making of plans, the diagnosis of a patient's illness, etc., can all be considered as problems that can be answered through a process of searching. Consider the planning of a journey from southern England to the north of England by bus. You have at your disposal a timetable and the task is to find a series of connections that will take you from Southampton to Nottingham (we are assuming no direct connections). You could start at Southampton as the point of departure and look down the destinations column. You pick a destination and then move to that destination's page in the timetable. The destination now becomes your imagined point of departure and you select another destination. You continue in this fashion until you hit a departure that has a destination listed as Nottingham. This is a bit simplistic! In practice, you will most likely have some geographic knowledge and you will only consider intermediate destinations that lie in the direction of your final destination, Nottingham. You may even use multiple bookmarks as you search forward from Southampton to destination A, and then flick to Nottingham to see if there is a Nottingham-to-A connection; you continue in this back-and-forth manner in the hope of finding a common point where your forward and backward route plans meet.

Computer algorithms have been designed to mimic all these forms of searching. Let us consider a small puzzle known as the eight-tile puzzle. This puzzle has a grid with nine spaces and eight of the spaces are covered with a tile which is numbered. The space that is not covered is called a blank tile: it does not exist but it is a useful idea to simplify the problem description. The tiles are randomly arranged and the task is to get the tiles in a left-to-right, top-to-bottom order. The task is made boring and somewhat laborious: you place a blindfold on a friend and give your friend the puzzle to move tiles. Your friend moves a single tile and you inspect the result. The tiles are not configured in order and so you ask your friend to move, another tile; your friend decides which tile to move, not you. After the move you make another inspection, and this process continues until the tiles are configured in order.

The tiles are scrambled again into a random configuration. This time you keep a record of which moves have been made so your friend does not keep covering the same sequence of moves from any configuration. Your friend has been performing a blind search.

At each stage of searching there are a number of possible moves. To keep the description simple, we imagine that the blank tile moves, and it might have the option of moving up, down, right or left depending on where in the grid it is located. The only help you are giving to your friend is a signal of when the task has finished and preventing your friend from repeating a sequence of moves. Each tile configuration is known as a *state* and the task is to search for a goal state, the state which has the tiles in order. We could sketch a random start state and then consider which new states could be created by moving the blank tile. From each of these new states we could repeat the process. The idea is sketched in Figure 7.1. Only a few states are shown. From each state there emerge a number of lines, each line denoting a movement of the blank tile. The act of moving a tile results in a new state of the grid. If we continued our sketch for a large number of moves we would see that at several points throughout the sketch the goal state would be visible. Tracing the moves from the start state (the root) to one of these goal states provides a list of moves that defines a solution. Some lists would be shorter than others.

Algorithms for blind searching are easy to implement on a computer. The difficulty for some tasks is deciding on what contributes a state and how states are best represented. For the eight-tile puzzle the representation of states is easy, but the task becomes harder for real-world problems.

If you play the eight-tile puzzle on your own without a blindfold then you are likely to arrive at a quicker solution than your friend did with the blindfold. You

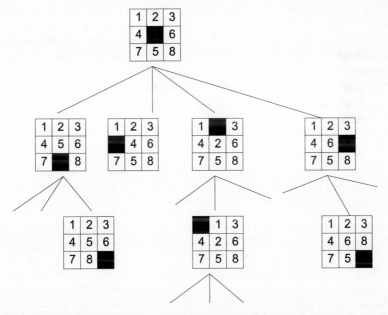

Figure 7.1 A few of the search states generated when trying to solve the eight-tile puzzle. The goal state is shown at the bottom left and right. Note that for the start state, moving the blank square up is the same as moving 2 down. Thinking of the puzzle in terms of moving the blank square is more convenient.

will make judgements as to whether a particular move looks like it will take you closer to the goal. This informed style of playing is known as *heuristic searching*. Searching a timetable with geographic knowledge is heuristic: knowledge is being used to guide the search. Devising algorithms to perform heuristic searching is not much more difficult than for blind searching. The really clever bit is defining the heuristics, that is, the rules of thumb.

Searching is a fundamental part of AI. The diagnosis of a patient's condition through the application of rules can be sketched as a search, and so too can aspects of natural language processing.

7.3.2 Production systems

The production system defines the fundamental ideas out of which expert systems and languages such as Prolog have grown. At the heart of a production system is a control procedure that remains fixed from one application to the next. The computation that a production system performs is controlled by a set of production rules and case-specific data. The production rules form a set of condition–action pairs which define the conditions that must exist for a rule to be enabled and the action that will result if a rule is fired. A *working memory* holds the current state of the world, and it is the current state that determines whether a rule's condition can be satisfied. The whole production cycle is fairly simple: test which rules can be satisfied with the state of the working memory, enable any satisfied rule, select a rule to fire from the set of enabled rules, and update the working memory according to the action of the rule that has fired.

The set of enabled rules is known as the *conflict set* and the strategy for selecting which enabled rule to fire is known as the *conflict-resolution strategy*. The whole process of selecting a rule to fire repeats until some halting condition is satisfied. A simple example is given in Figure 7.2. In this example

Production set:

1 $P \wedge Q \wedge R \Rightarrow goal$
2 $S \Rightarrow R$
3 $T \wedge W \Rightarrow Q$
4 $T \Rightarrow S$

Cycle	Working memory	Conflict set	Selected rule
0	T,W,P	3,4	3
1	T,W,P,Q	3,4	4
2	T,W,P,Q,S	2,3,4	2
3	T,W,P,Q,S,R	1,2,3,4	1
4	T,W,P,Q,S,R,goal	1,2,3,4	Halt

Figure 7.2 The production system steps involved in concluding the goal. T, W and P exist as facts at the start.

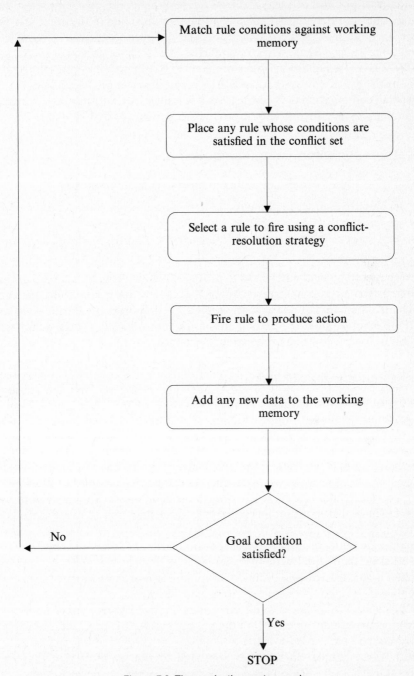

Figure 7.3 The production system cycle.

the conflict-resolution strategy is one of *recency*, which simply means select the rule that has not previously had its condition satisfied and in the event of a tie make an arbitrary selection. It is up to the designer to specify the conflict-resolution strategy. Some standard strategies exist such as recency or *specificity* (a rule with more conditions takes preference) but the reader must appreciate that the details of any system are left to the designer: a production system is a general computational procedure that is subject to tailoring as required. A summary of the operation of a production system is given in Figure 7.3.

7.4 Representation using symbols

To build intelligent systems, a representation language should be:

- expressive enough to allow the representation of all states in the world;
- concise so that the computation remains manageable;
- of a form suitable to facilitate inferencing so that the model of the world can change state.

Logic is used by mathematicians to prove a statement true or false. All of the main representation languages including Rules, Semantic nets and Frames can be transformed into a logic form known as first-order predicate calculus (FOPC). A brief look at FOPC is given after introducing a more simplified version of logic known as propositional calculus.

7.4.1 Propositional calculus

A proposition is a sentence that can be assigned a value of TRUE or FALSE. For example, 'Today it rained' or 'Copper is a metal' are either true or false statements. With propositional calculus we can symbolize sentences, create complex sentences from other sentences using connectives, and perform inferencing to find the truth value of a sentence. The syntax of propositional calculus describes how to construct sentences (including complex expressions); the grammar defines rules that are used to decide if a sentence is syntactically correct. The semantics of propositional calculus defines how to relate sentences to the value TRUE or FALSE.

An atomic sentence is a simple proposition such as 'Today it rained' and it will often be symbolized with an upper-case letter such as P or Q. A complex sentence is constructed using connectives to join two or more atomic sentences. Parentheses '(' and ')' are used to stress the order of precedence when combining atomic sentences with connectives. Table 7.1 gives an explanation of the connectives and Table 7.2 lists the grammar rules for propositional logic. The grammar can be used to parse a sentence and check that it is syntactically correct. For example, an informal approach to test by inspection that the expression $((P \wedge Q) \wedge R) \Rightarrow S$ is a syntactically correct sentence is shown in Table 7.3.

Table 7.1 *Logic connectives*

Connective	Example
∧ (AND) known as conjunction.	Today it rained AND I got wet. $P \wedge Q$, where P stands for the conjunct 'Today it rained' and Q for the conjunct 'I got wet'.
∨ (OR) known as disjunction.	Sally went to the shop OR Tom went to the shop. $P \vee Q$, where P stands for the disjunct 'Sally went to the shop' and Q for the disjunct 'Tom went to the shop'.
¬ (NOT) known as negation.	An elephant is NOT pink. $\neg P$, where P stands for 'An elephant is pink'.
⇒ (IMPLIES) known as implication and also as an if–then statement.	If I was outside AND it rained THEN I got wet. $(P \wedge Q) \Rightarrow R$, where P stands for 'I was outside', Q stands for 'It rained' and R stands for 'I got wet'.
⇔ (EQUIVALENT) known as equivalence or sometimes as double implication.	Expressions either side of this connective should be logically equivalent.

Table 7.2 *Grammar rules for propositional logic*

Grammar rule	Explanation
Sentence → Atomic − sentence |Complex − sentence	A sentence is either atomic or complex.
Atomic − setence → $P\|Q\|R\|$ . . . Atomic − sentence → TRUE|FALSE	An atomic sentence is symbolized with a capital letter usually from the latter part of the alphabet. An atomic sentence can also be symbolized with the values TRUE or FALSE.

Complex − sentence →
    Sentence Connective Sentence
    |¬Sentence|(Sentence)
	A complex sentence is constructed from two other sentences and a connective. The negation of a sentence is still a sentence and parenthesizing a sentence still results in a sentence.

Connective → ∧|∨|¬|⇒|⇔	A connective is any of the logic symbols from Table 7.1.

The semantics of propositional calculus is defined using a *truth table*. The connectives, apart from negation, are binary and therefore two symbols need to be used in the definitions. A sentence can take the value TRUE or FALSE and so for binary connectives there are four possible combinations, as shown in Table 7.4.

Table 7.3 *Example parse*

Position in parse	Explanation
$(P \wedge Q) \wedge R) \Rightarrow S$	According to the first rule a sentence is either atomic or complex. Clearly this expression is not atomic and so we test it for being complex.
$((P \wedge Q) \wedge R \Rightarrow S$	The right-hand side is simply S and S is an atomic sentence according to the second rule.
$((P \wedge Q) \wedge R)$	We need to show that $(P \wedge Q) \wedge R$ is a complex sentence.
$(P \wedge Q) \wedge R$	Again, testing against the form 'Sentence Connective Sentence', R is certainly a sentence because it is atomic.
$(P \wedge Q)$	We need to show that $P \wedge Q$ is a complex sentence.
$P \wedge Q$	Once again we have the form 'Sentence Connective Sentence' and both P and Q are sentences.

Table 7.4 *Truth table*

P	Q	$\neg P$	$P \wedge Q$	$P \vee Q$	$P \Rightarrow Q$	$P \Leftrightarrow Q$
TRUE	TRUE	FALSE	TRUE	TRUE	TRUE	TRUE
TRUE	FALSE	FALSE	FALSE	TRUE	FALSE	FALSE
FALSE	TRUE	TRUE	FALSE	TRUE	TRUE	FALSE
FALSE	FALSE	TRUE	FALSE	FALSE	TRUE	TRUE

Most of the connective definitions are intuitive. For example, 'It rained today AND it did NOT rain today' is obviously FALSE, and is confirmed in the truth table when looking up the possible assignments for TRUE $\wedge$ FALSE or FALSE $\wedge$ TRUE. The definition of implication often poses difficulty because we intuitively attempt to make an interpretation based on our general understanding of language. For example, we may say that the sentence 'If 5 is even then my car is pink' (of the form $P \Rightarrow Q$) is false because it makes no sense. However, checking the definition for implication will show that the expression is true regardless of whether your car is pink or not: we know that '5 is even' to be false and so the combination is either FALSE $\Rightarrow$ TRUE (car is pink) or FALSE $\Rightarrow$ FALSE (car is not pink). We tend to interpret if–then expressions as causal and therefore the sentence 'If 5 is even then my car is pink' makes no sense because the definition of the number 5 has no effect on the colour of my car; the point to remember is that implication in propositional calculus does not demand that there be any relevant connection between the sentences on either side of the implication connective. With implication, knowing P to be false will not help us to decide on the truth of Q. For example, 'If the battery is flat then the car will not start' enables us to deduce that it is true that 'the car will not start' if it is true that 'the battery is flat' but the rule tells us nothing of the car's

Table 7.5 *Inference rules for propositional logic*

Rule	Explanation
Modus ponens: $$\frac{A \Rightarrow B, A}{B}$$	If the antecedent (*A*) is known to be TRUE then the conclusion (B) will be TRUE.
AND elimination: $$\frac{A \wedge B}{A}, \frac{A \wedge B}{B}$$	Knowing *A* AND *B* to be TRUE must mean *A* is TRUE and similarly for *B*.
OR introduction $$\frac{A}{A \vee B}, \frac{B}{A \vee B}$$	Given that *A* is TRUE then *A* OR *B* must be TRUE, and similarly for knowing *B* to be TRUE.
AND introduction $$\frac{A \quad B}{A \wedge B}$$	Given that *A* is TRUE and *B* is TRUE then *A* AND *B* must be TRUE.
Double negation $$\frac{\neg\neg A}{A}$$	If *A* is NOT NOT TRUE then it is TRUE.
Unit resolution $$\frac{A \vee B, \neg B}{A}, \frac{A \vee B, \neg A}{B}$$	Given that *A* OR *B* is TRUE and NOT *B* then *A* must be TRUE. Similarly, if NOT *A* is given then *B* must be TRUE.
Resolution $$\frac{A \vee B, \neg B \vee C}{A \vee C}$$	Given *A* OR *B* and NOT *B* OR *C*, because *B* cannot be both TRUE and FALSE then either *A* OR *C* must be TRUE.

ability to start if we know that 'the battery is not flat': the car may not start for a number of other reasons. If this is still somewhat confusing, it is best to think of $P \Rightarrow Q$ simply as enabling us to infer that Q is TRUE if we know P to be TRUE.

There are a number of inference rules for propositional logic, and these are shown in Table 7.5.

EXAMPLE 7.1

We are told the following.

> If a car has a flat battery then it will not start. If John's car will not start and it is after 8 a.m. then John will miss the train. One morning after 8 a.m. John's car had a flat battery.

Using inference rules of logic, show that John missed the train.

SOLUTION 7.1

The information can be symbolized as follows:

P: car has flat battery
Q: car will not start
R: after 8 a.m.
S: John has missed the train

Rule 1 $P \Rightarrow Q$
Rule 2 $Q \wedge R \Rightarrow S$

We are given P and R as TRUE. The task is to prove S. The proof proceeds as follows:

1	P	Given.
2	R	Given.
3	Q	From step 1, and rule 1 using modus ponens.
4	$Q \wedge R$	From step 3 and 2, and using AND introduction.
5	S	From step 4 and rule 2 using modus ponens.

7.4.2 Predicate calculus

Propositional calculus assumes that the world can be modelled as facts. For any sizeable application, propositional calculus is not suitable. Consider, for example, the number of statements that would be required if we were to model 50 or more people being late for work. A language is required that is more expressive in that it allows generalized expressions. Predicate calculus (or, more strictly, FOPC) extends the language of propositional calculus in that the world is considered to be made up of objects, relations and properties. The language allows generalized statements by introducing variables, and quantifiers that permit properties to be defined over a collection of objects. Consider the statement 'If a horse is owned by John then that horse is a thoroughbred'. The statement refers to a collection of objects, namely horses owned by John, and avoids making reference to any instance (that is, to one of John's horses). The statement is generalized and avoids the need specifically to state the case for each one of John's horses (Shamrock is owned by John therefore Shamrock is a thoroughbred, Tennyson is owned...). We can paraphrase the statement and say 'All horses owned by John are thoroughbreds'. A quantifier (all) is in place to indicate that the property 'Thoroughbred' applies to the complete collection of John's horses. The word own(ed) is a binary predicate that describes a relationship between John and a horse and the 'Thoroughbred' is a unary predicate that describes a property of a horse. In predicate calculus the statement 'All horses owned by John are thoroughbreds' is symbolized as

$$\forall x (\text{Horse}(x) \wedge \text{Own}(\text{John}, x)) \Rightarrow \text{Thoroughbred}(x)$$

The symbol $\forall$ is known as the *universal quantifier* and is read as 'for all' or 'every'. Predicate calculus defines another symbol, $\exists$, known as the *existential quantifier* and is read as 'there exists'. For example, if we say that 'John owns a thoroughbred horse' then all we know is that there exists at least one horse (maybe more) in John's collection that is a thoroughbred; the statement is expressed in predicate notation as

$$\exists x \; \text{Horse}(x) \wedge \text{Own}(\text{John}, x) \wedge \text{Thoroughbred}(x)$$

Predicate calculus provides a more concise language than natural language. Several sentences in natural language will reduce to the same sentence in predicate notation. Predicate calculus also reduces ambiguity. For example, 'All horses are not thoroughbreds' could be confused with 'Not all horses are thoroughbreds'; the confusion can be resolved by knowing that other breeds of horse exist. A predicate representation of each sentence highlights the difference: $\forall$horses $\neg$Thoroughbred(horse) and $\neg \forall$horses Thoroughbred(horse). The first sentence really states that all thoroughbreds are extinct (none exist) and the second sentence states that 'it is not true that every horse is a thoroughbred'.

7.4.3 Other symbol languages

There are many representation languages that have much in common. The popular languages such as FOPC, Frames and Semantic nets are essentially equivalent and share a number of key features:

- *objects* such as ball, person, boat, bicycle and philosopher;
- *relations* between objects, such as John is the father of Kim, or the train pulls the coach;
- *properties*, such as my car is green, David is six feet tall.

They really only differ in their syntax. Syntax is important in that one formalism may be more appropriate than another for conveying information. For example, it is easier to find a route between two London Underground stations using a graphical network than a sentence description of connected stations. Our choice of language should be expressive so that we can convey all the knowledge that needs to be conveyed, yet concise to allow efficient computation. The language should also allow the deduction of new knowledge from existing knowledge.

7.4.4 Prolog

Prolog is not a formal representation language, but its syntax is used in the next chapter and so it is introduced here.

Prolog is an AI programming language that represents data as a set of relationships between objects. A Prolog program consists of a list of facts and rules, and it is an attractive language since it has a built-in inference mechanism that will provide answers to questions about the knowledge that has been programmed. The syntax of Prolog is based on predicate calculus. A relationship such as 'John loves Mary' is written as

love(john, mary)

The predicate (that is, the relation) and objects of the relationship must begin with a lower-case letter. The above relationship is treated as a fact and other examples of facts are:

metal(copper)	copper is a metal
play(john, mary, tennis)	John and Mary play tennis

A variable begins with an upper-case character. When a variable refers to a constant (that is, an actual instance, such as john), the variable is said to be *instantiated*. A variable can become instantiated when expressions match. For example, suppose the database holds love(john, mary). The following questions can be asked:

Who loves mary?
loves(X, mary)
answer X = john   X is instantiated to john

Who is it that john loves?
love(john, X)
answer X = mary

Who loves whom?
love(X Y)
answer X = john, Y = mary

Rules are expressed using a backward notation in the form 'conclusion if condition' as opposed to 'if condition then conclusion'. For example,

uncle(X, Y) :- father(Z, Y), brother(Z, X)

The term ':-' stands for IF and the term ',' stands for AND. So the above rule states that

X is Y's uncle if Z is Y's father and Z is the brother of X

An example instantiation of this rule is shown in Figure 7.4.

A variable is local to a clause (that is, a fact or rule): a variable with the same name appearing in two different rules will be treated by Prolog as having different names.

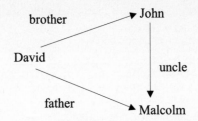

uncle(john, malcolm) :- father(david, malcolm), brother(david, john).

Figure 7.4 Prolog rule that is satisfied by the semantic representation shown in the diagram.

Prolog works by unification. When Prolog attempts to prove a goal it will search for the first clause that can be matched. For a match, two clauses must:

- have the same relation;
- have the same number of arguments;
- match on each argument.

Arguments match as follows:

1 Constant match: two constants match if they are identical strings.
2 Constant with a variable: if a variable is not instantiated then the variable will match any constant and will be instantiated to that constant; an instantiated variable will match a constant according to 1.
3 Two variables: two free variables (not instantiated) always match, and if at a later stage one variable becomes instantiated to a constant then the other variable will also be instantiated to that constant.

Example matches are shown in Table 7.6

EXAMPLE 7.2

Given the Prolog program listed below, explain how Prolog answers

?-uncle(john, X)

Table 7.6 *Pattern matching in Prolog*

Expression 1	Expression 2	Match
love(john, mary)	love(john, mary)	yes
love(john, X)	love(john, mary)	X = mary
love(john, mary)	like(john, mary)	no
love(X, Y)	love(john, mary)	X = john Y = mary
love(john, mary)	love(X, X)	no
love(X, mary) and X = john	love(Y, mary)	Y = X = john
hit(john, chris)	hit(john, chris, stick)	no

where the ?- is Prolog's prompt. The program listing is as follows

```
1 father(david, malcolm).
2 uncle(graham, malcolm).
3 brother(david, john).
4 uncle(X, Y) :- father(Z, Y), brother(Z, X).
```

Line numbers are shown for convenience.

SOLUTION 7.2

Prolog searches for a clause with the predicate 'uncle' and two arguments. The first occurrence is found at line 2 but the match fails because the first argument 'graham' does not match 'john'. The second clause containing 'uncle' is found at line 4 but for Prolog to succeed in proving its goal (the goal is to show that John is someone's uncle) the right-hand side of the clause must be satisfied: there needs to be a match for father(Z, Y) and brother(Z, X). The X in the query is different to the X in the rule, and so we have:

$$\text{Query: uncle(john, X1)}$$

to be matched against uncle(X2, Y) which is the head of the rule at line 4. There is a match with X2 = john and Y = X1 (or X1 = Y). The task is now to prove father(Z, X1) and brother(Z, john). The father(Z, X1) matches line 1 with Z = david and X1 = malcolm. The task now is to prove brother(david, john), which is satisfied by line 3. Prolog responds with X = malcolm.

7.5 Natural language understanding

Communication for humans using everyday language is an apparently effortless task, and yet any computer simulation falls well below the natural capability of a young schoolchild. Natural language understanding (NLU) systems (that is, machine simulations) have been built that exhibit a remarkable degree of practical utility. For example, it is possible to build a computerized flight-booking system that interfaces with a user using natural language; such a system can respond correctly to the majority of user requests. The desire for language processing systems becomes apparent when one considers the opportunities offered by the rapid growth in telecommunications. On-line banking is becoming more common, and there is growing interest in the development of automated agents that can search and sift through a vast amount of data on the Internet. All these applications, though, are restricted to limited domains. This domain restriction cuts complexity by reducing the size of vocabulary and making more manageable the assignment of meaning to a request. Although the array of domain-specific applications for NLU will grow over the next few years, it is not possible to foresee when a machine's language processing ability is likely to approach the competence level of a human. Natural language is such an expressive form of communication that it presents numerous variables for the computer scientist to consider. A few examples are listed in Table 7.7.

A little thought about how you attach meaning to a sentence or resolve ambiguous statements will serve to emphasize that NLU depends heavily on the availability of a large database of world knowledge. Many instances arise where we cannot be sure that our interpretation of any situation is correct, but knowledge of the world gives us a degree of confidence and also enables us to modify our interpretation in the light of further information.

Consider the sentence

Jane hit the boy with the ball.

Taken in isolation, we may assume that Jane kicked or threw the ball and it hit the boy. We would soon modify our interpretation if told 'Jane was watching the football match when she threw her hat at the players'.

As with most complex tasks, the implementation of NLU on a computer is broken down into a number of levels. The three levels that occupy much of NLU discussion are the *syntactic* level, the *semantic* level and the *pragmatic* level. The syntactic level is concerned with the way words are structured into phrases and how phrases are structured into sentences. Grammar rules are typically used to check that a sentence is allowed (that is to say, is grammatical) and to split the

Table 7.7 *Some difficulties with processing natural language*

Type of problem	Example	Explanation
Saying the same thing in two different ways	1 Stuart hit the ball. 2 The ball was hit by Stuart.	(1) is expressed in active form. (2) is the passive form of (1).
With-clause role	1 The girl hit the boy with the stick. 2 The girl hit the boy with the dog.	In (1) the with clause denotes an instrument of hitting whereas in (2) the with-clause modifies the boy (i.e., adds more description).
Many words have multiple functions	1 The green flies. 2 The aeroplane flies.	In (1) 'flies' refers to insects and is a noun whereas in (2) 'flies' is a form of the verb 'fly'.
Subject–verb number agreement	1 Racing cars is dangerous. 2 Racing cars are dangerous.	(1) refers to the act of driving a car whereas (2) implies you should keep clear of a race track.
Word order	1 The dog ate the cat. 2 The cat ate the dog.	In (1) the cat was eaten where in (2) the dog was eaten.

sentence into constituent parts. The semantic and pragmatic levels are to do with meaning. At the semantic level the propositional content is extracted; a logic form is often used to express the propositional content. For example,

> John kicked the ball.
> Did John kick the ball?

both have the same propositional content which in Prolog notation can be expressed as

> kick(john, ball)

With an ability to automate the syntactic and semantic analysis, we can now state

> John kicked the ball.   kick(john, ball)

and then ask

> Who kicked the ball?   kick(X, ball)
> What did John kick?   kick(john, X)
> Who kicked what?   kick(X, Y)

Pragmatic analysis deals with the interpretation of a sentence in context. The 'He' in the sentence

> He scored a goal

can only be resolved in context (that is, resolved using the surrounding sentences). To answer 'Who scored the goal?' we need to resolve who 'He' is an index for. The intention of a speaker is also context-dependent. The sentence

> Can you make a cup of tea?

is often meant as a request for a cup of tea to be made but it could literally mean 'Are you capable of making tea?'. Context is also used to restrict the sense of a word. The word 'loves' in everyday use has a sense expressed in the form

> love(human, object)

This sense admits expressions such as 'John loves Mary', 'John loves work', and 'John loves chocolate'. In the context of human relations 'love' may be restricted to

> love(human, human)

and in this sense we may assume that 'Candy' in

> love(john, candy)

is a human subject rather than a sweet. The restriction in this case has resolved a potential ambiguity between 'Candy' being a sweet and 'Candy' being human.

We now give brief consideration to syntactic and semantic processing.

7.5.1 Syntactic analysis

A piece of text is composed of sentences, and each sentence is composed of phrases which may contain sub-phrases that eventually terminate as words. A grammar governs the way in which words and phrases are allowed to combine into sentences. A grammar can be expressed using any one of a number of representational languages, but a frequently used format is the rewrite rule. An example grammar using rewrite rules is given in Figure 7.5. Figure 7.6 expresses the structure of the sentence 'the dog ran across the road'.

```
S   →NP VP|NP V
NP →D AP|D N|NP PP
PP →P NP
VP →V NP|V PP
AP →A AP|A N
```

Figure 7.5 Sample grammar expressed using rewrite rules. S denotes sentence, N noun, A adjective, P preposition, D determiner, NP noun phrase, VP verb phrase, AP adjective phrase, PP preposition phrase.

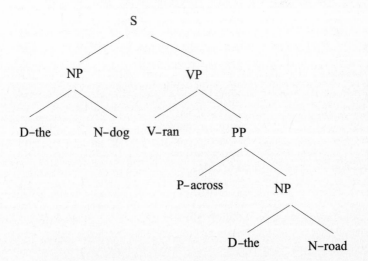

Figure 7.6 The parse tree for 'The dog ran across the road'.

A sentence is parsed to extract the phrase structure and to test that the sentence conforms to the grammar. A lexicon is also required for sentence parsing. The lexicon gives the category of a word (N, V, P, A, D). A parse can be viewed as a search where back-up states are maintained on a stack so that a recovery from a dead end can be made.

EXAMPLE 7.3

Illustrate how the sentence 'The dog ran across the road' can be parsed as a search. Use the following grammar:

$$S \rightarrow NP\ VP$$
$$NP \rightarrow D\ AP | D\ N$$
$$PP \rightarrow P\ NP$$
$$VP \rightarrow V\ PP$$
$$AP \rightarrow A\ N$$

and the following lexicon:

$$D \rightarrow the \quad N \rightarrow dog | road \quad V \rightarrow ran \quad P \rightarrow across$$

SOLUTION 7.3

The process is shown in Table 7.8 and the states generated in Figure 7.7.

Table 7.8 *The parse of 'The dog ran across the road' viewed as a search*

Current attempt	Word stack	To visit stack	Backup stack
S → NP VP	the dog ran across the road	NP VP	
NP → D AP	the dog ran across the road	D AP VP	NP → D N
D → the	dog ran across the road	AP VP	NP → D N
AP → A N	dog ran across the road	VP	NP → D N
dog does not match A so backup			
NP → D N	the dog ran across the road	D N VP	
D → the	dog ran across the road	N VP	
N → dog	ran across the road	VP	
VP → V PP	ran across the road	V PP	
V → ran	across the road	PP	
PP → P NP	across the road	P NP	
P → across	the road	NP	
NP → D AP	the road	D AP	NP → D N
D → the	road	AP	NP → D N
AP → A N	road	A N	NP → D N
road is not an A so backup			
NP → D N	the road	D N	
D → the	road	N	
N → road			

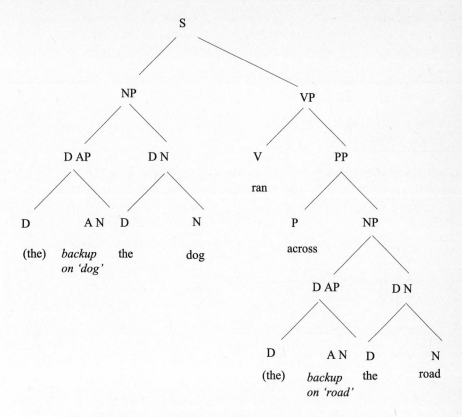

Figure 7.7 States generated in parsing 'The dog ran across the road'.

Algorithms for parsing have been extensively researched since parsing is a basic requirement for many aspects of computing, whether it be compiling a program or checking the syntax of a database query. The example sentences given here are somewhat trivial but any NLU system will require a grammar that is enhanced to handle such things as number agreement and tense. These enhancements are beyond the scope of this text, but the interested reader will find guidance under the further reading section at the end of this chapter.

7.5.2 Semantic analysis

Semantic analysis is often assimilated into the parsing stage by adding features to the grammar rules and using pattern matching. There is only space here to hint at the way of extracting propositional content in a Prolog form.

The grammar

```
S → NP VP
NP → N
N → name
VP → V NP

name → mary|john
verb → loves
```

will accept the sentence 'John loves Mary'. The Prolog form is

```
loves(john, mary)
```

To extract this form during parsing, the grammar is enhanced with features

```
S(sem-vp sem-np) → NP(sem-np) VP(sem-vp)
NP(sem-np) → N(sem-np)
N(sem-n) → (sem-n)
VP(sem-v sem-np) → V(sem-v) NP(sem-np)

name(sem-n) → mary("mary")
name(sem-n) → john("john")
verb(sem-v)  → love(λy.λx.love(x, y))
```

The above verb entry has an expression in what is known as *lambda calculus*. Here we use it to perform a simple operation known as *lambda reduction* to simplify an expression. For example, an expression of the form

$$((\lambda \times Px)a)$$

can be reduced to 'Pa'. So the expression $\lambda y.\lambda x.love(x, y)$ formulated with $((\lambda y.\lambda x.love(x, y))$ "mary") reduces to $\lambda x.love(x, mary)$ and $((\lambda x.love(x, mary))$ "john") reduces to love(john, mary).

The lambda reduction works in a left-to-right order and its purpose is simply to make the expression more readable (or recognizable).

With our simple example we can think of the matching of features as a series of function calls. The left-hand side of a rule is viewed as a function, with the right-hand side making a series of calls to other functions. This operation continues in a recursive fashion until a word is matched and a string is returned.

The sentence 'John loves Mary' will be parsed using a pseudo C notation with lambda reduction where appropriate. Note that some brackets in the grammar have been left out to keep the notation simple.

```
call S with "john loves mary"
    returns (λx.love(x, mary) john) = love(john, mary)

S(sem-vp sem-np) {
  NP(sem-np)            john eventually returns from call to NP
  VP(sem-vp)            (λy.λx.love(x, y) mary) = (λx.love(x, mary))
                        returns from call to VP
}
NP(sem-np) {
  N(sem-np)
}
N(sem-n) {
  name(sem-n)
}
name(sem-n) {
  if "john"
    return sem-n = "john"
  if "mary"
    return sem-n = "mary"
}
VP(sem-v sem-np) {
  V(sem-v)             (λy.λx.love(x, y)) is returned from call to V
  NP(sem-np)           mary is returned
}
V(sem-v) {
  sem-v = (λy.λx.love(x, y))
}
```

7.6 The symbol connectionist link

The idea of using neural networks to perform tasks which have been the traditional domain of symbolic AI appeals to engineers' intuition, not only because abstract architectures of the brain may yield unexpected solutions but also because neural networks have a number of desirable properties. Neural networks learn a task by adapting to fed stimuli. A system based on learning has the opportunity to induce knowledge automatically and to discover task-specific knowledge that cannot easily be prescribed by a set of rules (for example, how to ride a bicycle). A net rarely provides a black and white judgement, instead it provides a graded response and graded responses seem more appropriate for everyday tasks. Neural nets can also exhibit graceful degradation in that they can still perform a task (albeit at a reduced level) if some part of the architecture is damaged: in other words, neural nets can sometimes still perform even if part of the architecture no longer functions. Finally, neural nets can be massively parallel architectures that have the potential to offer a hike in performance over serial-based machines.

Symbol systems also have their attraction. We communicate using symbols and much knowledge is conveyed in the process of this communication. For example, if you are told that you will be killed if you touch a live rail on a railway track, then, barring complete stupidity or misfortune, you will heed the warning. Knowledge expressed as rules can save lives in situations which have not been previously experienced. An aircraft pilot who unintentionally enters a spin is faced with a life-threatening situation and although practice of recovery from intentional spins will help the pilot cope, it is possible for an inexperienced pilot to recover if that pilot knows the rules. Knowledge communicated in symbol form can also speed up learning. A difficult phase of training for any pilot is learning to land. A good instructor can provide rules of thumb to help the novice pilot and can also feed back instructions to help correct poor performance.

So, both the symbol and connectionist paradigms have attractive features for building intelligent systems. It is hardly surprising, then, to discover that much research has been (and continues to be) carried out into linking traditional or symbolic AI with neural nets. These links vary quite widely in scope, but perhaps a question of central importance to many connectionists is whether neural nets can be constructed to perform high-level cognitive tasks such as natural language processing and planning.

The material covered in the next chapter was motivated by the philosophical debate that emerged during the second half of the 1980s (see, for example, Fodor and Pylyshyn, 1988). All the early applications of neural nets, following renewed interest in the 1980s, tackled low-level pattern recognition problems which essentially involved mapping a set of input data onto to some appropriate output response. Also, because there was much discussion with regard to neural nets as cognitive models it is hardly surprising that some philosophers and cognitive psychologists started to question the capabilities of these first-generation nets. Since that time we have discovered that some of the criticism was founded on ignorance of how to extract the required performance from a neural net. It has to be admitted, though, that satisfactory answers to these criticisms have yet to be found but there is a new sense of optimism as the connectionist domain continues to mature.

Three features that are central to the success of the symbol paradigm are compositional structures, structure-sensitive processing and generalization. All three features are interlinked.

Compositional structures can be mapped as hierarchical structures where the whole structure is made up of parts. Trees are typical examples, and so too are the inheritance and aggregation models used by software engineers. Compositional structuring is fundamental to all forms of engineering: a complex task is normally tackled by decomposing the task into parts. Compositional analysis plays a major part in NLU, as we saw in Section 7.5. The phrase structure of a sentence is presented as a hierarchy of sub-parts and semantic analysis assumes that the meaning of a whole sentence can be found by combining the meaning of its parts.

The transformation of $\neg(P \wedge Q)$ to its logical equivalent $(\neg P \vee \neg Q)$ is an example of an operation that is sensitive to structure. If P and Q are replaced with R and S the operation is still possible since the structural form is what matters: $\neg(R \wedge S)$ will transform to its logical equivalent $(\neg R \vee \neg S)$. The operation can also be performed on more complex expressions because the whole expression can be decomposed into parts. For example, $\neg((P \vee R) \wedge Q)$ is still of the form $\neg(A \wedge Q)$ and so the logical equivalent is $(\neg(P \vee R) \vee \neg Q)$.

The abstraction of generalized expressions is also a natural part of the symbol paradigm. The arguments in love(animate, object) admit a whole host of objects as suitable constituents of the relationship love. This form of relationship permits a system to exhibit a systematic behaviour. If a system is systematic it should allow semantic (and syntactic) generalizations. A systematic system that understands 'john loves mary' will also understand 'mary loves john'.

Our connectionist treatment in the next chapter will concentrate on these features, which are seen as central to the symbolic domain.

7.7 Summary

Traditional AI has put a great deal of effort into researching representational issues. A key component of any intelligent system is an ability to adapt to a changing environment – in other words, to learn. Traditional AI systems use symbol structures to represent the domain knowledge, and computation can be viewed as a series of operations that are applied to these structures during the process of searching for a solution. Some of the key points recommending traditional AI are as follows:

- Knowledge is visible.
- Component structures can be combined to build larger more complex structures. That is, larger structures can be composed from small structures and in turn these larger structures can be broken into smaller ones.
- Symbol representations facilitate generalization and the abstraction of knowledge.

7.8 Further reading

If you are new to the subject of AI then a good book to begin with is that by Cawsey (1998) which is in the same series of books as this one. The philosophical introduction to AI by Copeland (1993) provides a good high-level general introduction to the subject. The text by Dean *et al.* (1995) is a good AI text with some interesting examples, but it is somewhat weighted towards the Lisp language. Russell and Norvig's (1995) book is an excellent and comprehensive AI text.

One of the most ambitious and probably the largest AI project undertaken to date is known as CYC. CYC is a massive knowledge base that has been built to hold the type of knowledge that would be required to access and make sense of information contained in an encyclopaedia. CYC contains a great deal of general knowledge, the sort of knowledge that we use every day but which appears to require no conscious effort to apply. For example, when you are told someone's date of birth you will also know that the birthday for that person is celebrated on the same day every year. There is though, a lot more to CYC. A good deal of CYC's knowledge has been programmed by a team of knowledge engineers, but CYC has now reached the stage where it can learn a lot of knowledge for itself by reading text. CYC needs some help with understanding the text but a major goal of the CYC team is natural language understanding. The best source of information on CYC is the Web site for CYC:

http://www.cyc.com/

7.9 Exercises

1 Show that the expression

$$((P \Rightarrow Q) \wedge R) \Rightarrow S$$

will be parsed as legal according to the grammar in Table 7.2.

2 Use a truth table to show that $\neg((P \vee R) \wedge Q)$ is equivalent to $(\neg(P \vee R) \vee \neg Q)$.

3 In Figure 7.2 a production system was used to prove the goal in the following rules given that T, W and P were TRUE.

```
1   P ∧ Q ∧ R ⇒ goal
2   S ⇒ R
3   T ∧ W ⇒ Q
4   T ⇒ S
```

Use the inference rules of propositional logic to prove the goal.

4

```
S → NP VP|NP V
NP → D AP|D N|NP PP
PP → P NP
VP → V NP|V PP
AP → A AP|A N
```

Use the above grammar to sketch the parse trees for:
(a) The little dog barked.
(b) The horse jumped over the fence.
5 Show the search states generated during a parse of the sentences in Question 4.
6 How would the grammar in Question 4 have to be modified to accept the sentence 'John found the book' as legal?
7 Given the Prolog database:

```
partOf(flap, wing)
partOf(aileron, wing)
partOf(wing, aeroplane)
```

paraphrase the following questions and show how Prolog would respond to these questions.
(a) partOf(flap, wing).
(b) partOf(wing, X).
(c) partOf(X, wing).
8 Suppose the Prolog code in Question 7 is enhanced with

```
partOf(X, Y) :- partOf(Z, Y), partOf(X, Z)
```

(a) How would the program respond to partOf(flap, aeroplane)? Trace the matching process.
(b) Can you think of any potential problem with the above rule?

CHAPTER 8

Synthesizing symbols with neural networks

Aim: To introduce some of the links between traditional AI and neural networks.

Objectives: You should be able to:

discuss some of the potential advantages of combining symbolic and connectionist (neural network) representations;
describe what local and distributed representations are;
discuss some of the approaches being used by neural network researchers to tackle natural language understanding;
describe what is meant by compositional and systematic representations;
explain the notion of 'symbol grounding'.

Prerequisites: Chapters 1–7.

8.1 Neural networks in symbolic cloaks

In this chapter we will not look at new AI *per se*, only at the connectionist part and at some representative samples of recent work in order to illustrate the fundamental concepts. The term *connectionist* will often be used to refer to neural networks and the term *connectionism* to refer to the general paradigm of neural networks. Connectionists are people who wish to harness the computational ability of neural networks and are not directly concerned with biological realism, unlike other neural network researchers who use neural networks in an attempt to explain computational processes within the brain.

There are several notable connectionist models (see the list of further reading in Section 8.8) that are designed to encode and process symbol-style structures. This chapter will first describe a neural network architecture known as *recursive autoassociative memory* (RAAM). There are several motivating reasons for taking a close look at RAAM. First, RAAM can be explored with little or no need for mathematical description. Second, when RAAM emerged it was seen as a useful weapon in the rebuttal of earlier criticisms that connectionist networks could not behave in a compositional and systematic way. Also, RAAM has caught the imagination of the connectionist community and there is a growing base of research and literature. Finally, and perhaps more importantly, it is a useful architecture for exploring some of the key issues.

After introducing RAAM and some issues to do with representation, two models for tackling natural language processing are introduced. These models are somewhat complicated architectures and the reader is not expected to gain a deep understanding of their implementation. The motivation for presenting these models and the later models on machine communication is to make the reader aware that neural net researchers are beginning to tackle some of the very difficult problems that have challenged traditional AI. Although it is very early days, these models give an insight into how complex systems will develop in the future out of basic neural architectures. We are really only just beginning to construct 'artificial neural systems' and early results suggest that there may be some surprises in store.

The important but difficult subjects of *abstract generalization* and *symbol grounding* are also introduced in this chapter.

The reader should not be put off if the material in this chapter proves difficult. Some of the concepts are difficult to comprehend and a real under-standing can only be gained from a willingness to explore the referenced literature. This chapter is meant to be more challenging than earlier chapters, but, above all, it is included to make the reader aware of some topics that are important and that are gradually receiving the attention they deserve.

8.2 Recursive autoassociation memory

The RAAM architecture was devised by Pollack (1990). The purpose of an RAAM is to provide a connectionist representation of symbol structures. The symbol structures are fixed-valence trees. The valence refers to the number of branches that emerge from each node and fixing the valence means that all nodes should have the same number of emergent branches.

Figure 8.1 lists a set of 15 binary trees (of valence 2). These trees in Figure 8.1 identify some phrase structures generated in accordance with the grammar rules listed below:

$$S \rightarrow NP\ VP | NP\ V$$
$$NP \rightarrow D\ AP | D\ N | NP\ PP$$
$$PP \rightarrow P\ NP$$
$$VP \rightarrow V\ NP | V\ PP$$
$$AP \rightarrow A\ AP | A\ N$$

where the symbols used have the same meanings as in Figure 7.5.

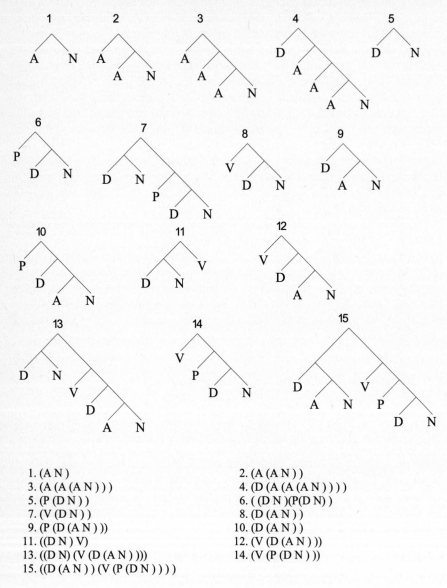

1. (A N)
3. (A (A (A N)))
5. (P (D N))
7. (V (D N))
9. (P (D (A N)))
11. ((D N) V)
13. ((D N) (V (D (A N))))
15. ((D (A N)) (V (P (D N))))

2. (A (A N))
4. (D (A (A (A N))))
6. ((D N)(P(D N))
8. (D (A N))
10. (D (A N))
12. (V (D (A N)))
14. (V (P (D N)))

Figure 8.1 These trees are taken from Pollack (1990). The trees show the phrase structure of sentences (or parts of a sentence). Note that many trees are sub-trees (or parts) of other trees. For example, tree 1 is a part of tree 2 and tree 2 is a part of tree 3; similarly, trees 8 and 14 are parts of tree 15.

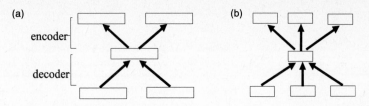

Figure 8.2 The architecture for (a) a binary RAAM and (b) a ternary RAAM.

An RAAM is basically an autoassociative backpropagation network (see Chapters 2 and 4). The input layer and output layer of an RAAM have units arranged into fields, with each field containing the same number of units. The number of fields is defined by the valence of the trees that are to be encoded and the number of units in the hidden layer matches the number of units in a single field. Figure 8.2 shows two example architectures.

For the moment we shall ignore the way in which an RAAM is trained and just see how it constructs a representation and how it decomposes the representation back into its constituent parts. If we take an RAAM that has been trained to represent a set of trees, we can think of that RAAM as providing two machines: the first layer of weights provides a machine to construct a representation of any tree, and the second layer of weights provides a machine that takes a constructed representation and reconstructs its parts; the first machine will be called an *encoder* and the second a *decoder*. The RAAM representation for a structure emerges from the activation values of the hidden layer. In the process of constructing a representation for the whole tree, an RAAM will generate a representation for every internal node (that is, every sub-tree). So, encoding ((D N)(P(D N))) leads to representations for (D N) and (P (D N)) being generated along the way. Trees are recursive structures and an RAAM forms its representations in a recursive manner by feeding back into the input layer, at specified times, the earlier formed representations of parts. The encoding of ((D N)(P(D N))) is illustrated in Figure 8.3 and its decoding into parts in Figure 8.4.

The terminal symbols (D, A, N, V and P) are presented to the network as vectors. A common technique is to use orthogonal vectors, which in this example means that each symbol is a vector with five elements because there are five symbols and each vector has a single element set to 1 and all other elements set to 0 (all vectors are to be different with one bit only set to 1). An example set of vectors is as follows:

$$
\begin{array}{llll}
\text{D} & 1\,0\,0\,0\,0 & \text{A} & 0\,1\,0\,0\,0 \\
\text{N} & 0\,0\,1\,0\,0 & \text{V} & 0\,0\,0\,1\,0 \\
\text{P} & 0\,0\,0\,0\,1 & &
\end{array}
$$

The dimension (number of bits) of the symbol vectors defines the minimum number of units within a field of the RAAM. The hidden layer, of course,

1.
(DN)'
D
N
The vectors that represent the symbols D and N are presented to the encoder part of the network. The resulting output is the 'compressed' (denoted by ') representation for (DN).
2.
(P(DN))'
P
(DN)'
The second stage is to present the 'compressed' representaton for (DN) (from stage 1) back into the netork along with the vector representation for P, to create (P(DN))'.
3.
((DN)(P(DN)))'
(DN)'
(P(DN))'
The third stage is to present the 'compressed' representaton for (DN) (from stage 1) along with (P(DN))' (from stage 2) into the netork to create the compressed representation for the whole tree – ((DN)(P(DN)))'.

Figure 8.3 The encoding of ((DN)(P(DN))). The same network is shown at the three different stages of encoding the representation.

1.
(DN)'
(P(DN))'
((DN)(P(DN)))'
The representation for the whole tree is presented to the decoder
2.
D
N
(DN)'
(DN)' from stage 1 is presented and decoded back into D and N
3.
P
(DN)'
(P(DN))
(P(DN))' from stage 1 is presented and decoded back into P and (DN)'
4.
D
N
(DN)'
(DN)' from stage 3 is presented and decoded back into D and N

Figure 8.4 The decoding of ((DN)(P(DN)))'. The same network is shown at the four different stages of decoding the representation.

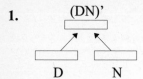

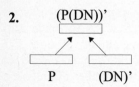

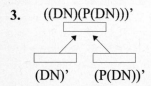

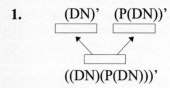

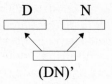

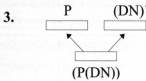

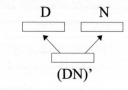

provides a compressed representation because the number of units in this layer is less than the number of input units. The amount of compression that can be achieved, however, depends on the particular training data set, and it may be necessary to pad the terminal symbol vectors with extra zeros. For example, the RAAM used to represent the trees in Figure 8.1 had a 20-10-20 architecture. Each field therefore had ten units which meant that the terminal symbol vectors needed padding with five zeros. In this example, we say that the code for a terminal is a 1-bit-in-5 padded with five zeros. Like most network architectures, the number of hidden units is determined through experimentation (finding an architecture that provides a satisfactory solution).

When decoding, a test is required to detect whether a pattern emerging on a field in the output layer is a terminal or requires storing for later feedback into the hidden layer. There are a number of possible ways to perform this test, but a simple approach with orthogonal symbols is to test whether a single unit is 1 with all others set to 0. If a terminal is not present the output can be fed back through the hidden layer.

8.2.1 Training an RAAM

Training proceeds as for any autoassociative network but with the requirement to feed back into the input layer previously constructed parts. The timing of this feedback is the same as for the construction explained above. The terminal symbols have their input vectors fixed at the outset, but since the weights continually adapt during training the representation of any non-terminal symbols must change. For example, the hidden representation for (D N) will change as training progresses since the weights are continually changing. This change amongst the training patterns is referred to as the *moving target* effect. When the network is near convergence the changes in these moving targets become very small.

When it comes to implementing an RAAM, the only added complication compared to a autoassociative backpropagation network is when previously formed hidden patterns should be fed back to the input layer. This matter of timing is easily resolved using a stack data structure to push and pop internal nodes. Representing a sequence with an RAAM is even easier. A sequence such as the word BRAIN can be represented as a tree of the form shown in Figure 8.5. The NIL terminal simply acts as a blank. The encoding starts, as usual, from the bottom up with B presented to the left input field and NIL to the right input field. Because the compressed representations only get fed to the right input field it is possible for the left and right input fields (and therefore output fields) to contain different numbers of units: the constraint is that the hidden layer and right input and output fields should be of the same size. With a sequence there is no need to store representations on a stack since previous compressed items are continually recirculated to the input layer.

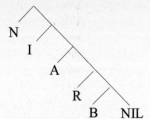

Figure 8.5 The representation of BRAIN as a tree.

EXAMPLE 8.1

1 Show the order of encoding and decoding of the binary tree

$$((D\ (A\ N))\ (V\ (P\ (D\ N)))) $$

2 For the training set given below, how many trees will an RAAM learn to represent?

$$(D\ (A\ (A\ (A\ N\ ))\ )\ ) $$
$$(\ (D\ N\ )(P(D\ N)\ ) $$
$$(V\ (D\ N\ )\ ) $$
$$(P\ (D\ (A\ N\ )\ )) $$
$$((D\ N\ )\ V) $$
$$((D\ N)\ (V\ (D\ (A\ N\ )\ ))) $$
$$((D\ (A\ N\ )\ )\ (V\ (P\ (D\ N\ )\ )\ )\ ) $$

SOLUTION 8.1

1 The order of encoding is given in Table 8.1 and of decoding in Table 8.2.
2 The total set of trees is illustrated in Figure 8.1.

Table 8.1 *Order of encoding for the binary tree in Example 8.1*

Left branch	Right branch	Hidden representation
D	N	(D N)′
P	(D N)′	(P (D N))′
V	(P (D N))′	(V (P (D N)))′
A	N	(A N)′
D	(A N)′	(D (A N))′
(D (A N))′	(V (P (D N)))′	((D (A N)) (V (P (D N))))′

Table 8.2 *Order of decoding for the binary tree in Example 8.1*

Hidden representation	Left branch	Right branch
((D (A N)) (V (P (D N))))'	(D (A N))'	(V (P (D N)))'
(D (A N))'	D	(A N)'
(A N)'	A	N
(V (P (D N)))'	V	(P (D N))'
(P (D N))'	P	(D N)'
(D N)'	D	N

8.3 Connectionist representations

The RAAM architecture takes variable-sized structures (that is, trees of different sizes) and maps them into fixed-width vectors. This form of mapping has a number of desirable properties which are now examined.

8.3.1 Local versus distributed

A local representation is where a network is designed so that individual units denote specific concepts. For example, one unit may stand for 'dog', another for 'horse', another for 'rabbit', another for 'wolf', and so on. More often the representation for a concept will be distributed. Figure 8.6 illustrates the idea of a distributed representation. A distributed representation is fault-tolerant to a certain degree since the loss of one or more units does not necessarily mean that the network has lost all of its representation of a particular concept. With a distributed representation a unit takes part in the representation of a concept (usually more than one). When a concept is represented in a distributed form it appears as a distributed pattern of activity. The left field of input units in a sequential RAAM act as a local representation when the terminal vectors are orthogonal: a single element in the terminal vector has the value 1 and so a single unit will be switched on. The compressed representations that develop on the hidden units are usually distributed in that a single letter from a word sequence, for example, is represented using more than one hidden unit. A distributed architecture is more economic than a local one for representing concepts. For example, a network with n binary units can only represent n concepts locally, whereas a distributed architecture can represent of the order of 2^n.

Some representations are distributed but not fully distributed. For example, a binary vector could be used to represent a concept where each bit denotes the presence of a feature. In the case of DOG, individual bits might represent the presence of features: has-tail, likes-bones, etc. With this form of representation, each concept is represented by more than one unit but a single unit only represents a single feature.

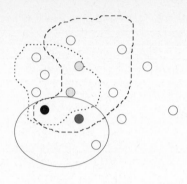

················ Denotes units involved in the concept 'dog'

------------ Denotes units involved in the concept 'wolf'

——————— Denotes units involved in the concept 'rabbit'

●   Unit involved in the concept 'dog', 'wolf'
and 'rabbit'

○   Unit involved in the concept 'dog' and 'wolf'

●   Unit involved in the concept 'wolf' and 'rabbit'

Figure 8.6 In a distributed representation units take part in representing more than one
concept, and a concept is represented by more than one unit.

A distributed representation does, however have some disadvantages. Suppose we train a neural network to make a decision as to whether someone should be allowed to borrow a nominated sum of money from a bank. The network may be trained on features such as: salary, current investments, assets, monthly outgoings, time with the bank, etc. We have a huge database of previous loan transactions available, and this database includes many examples of people who have defaulted. The network is trained and it appears to perform very well on a large test data set. We may then ask ourselves what knowledge the network is using to make its decision. A view of this knowledge would be useful: we may learn something new from the network and, more importantly, we could gain confidence in the network's ability to perform if it could explain how a decision is reached. To view the knowledge we need to know how the network represents information; this in turn leads to the question of what it is that individual units and weights represent, and with distributed representations the answer is not easily derived.

8.3.2 Spatial preservation of structure

Handling variable-sized structures with a fixed-sized network is not a trivial problem for connectionists. More of the neural computing systems of the future will have modular architectures where one network has to communicate with another network, and building systems around fixed-width interfaces can make the task easier. Also, concepts can be tested for similarity if all the representations are made to be the same width.

An RAAM maps a symbol structure into a spatial representation in that the n activations of the hidden units lie in an n-dimensional space. Symbol structures are composed by concatenating constituents. A simple example is the word BRAIN, which is composed as the concatenation of its individual letters. A vector representation of BRAIN can be obtained by concatenating the terminal codes. For example using a 1-bit-in-5 code for the letters, BRAIN could be represented by '10000 01000 00100 00010 00001'. The concatenation of binary codes to generate a type of connectionist representation is troublesome. For one thing, words of different length will have vectors of different sizes unless they are padded with zeros. Representing binary or higher-valence trees with sequential concatenation can ignore important information because the relative position of sub-trees is lost. For example, processing the trees from top to bottom results in (V (D N)) and ((D N) V) both being concatenated as 'DNV'. The way to overcome this is to assign a position for each tree node within the vector, but this technique becomes clumsy. RAAM composes representations in a functional way. The encoder can be thought of as a function that is recursively called. The composition of BRAIN is $f(Nf(If(Af(Rf(B\text{NIL}))))$, where $f(x)$ is the encoding of 'x' by a RAAM. With this form of functional mapping the sub-trees and whole tree become superimposed.

The structures of the trees in Figure 8.1 are governed by phrase grammar rules. The rules provide explicit knowledge of legal phrase structures and how they relate, but this knowledge becomes less explicit (or implicit) in the trees. For example, if you were asked to place the trees into groups you could use a number of criteria such as the tree depth, the number of common sub-trees or the number of terminals as a ratio of tree depth, etc. The grouping task is not trivial, and yet there is an explicit grouping determined by the grammar rules: that is, some trees fall into the S (sentence) group, others the NP (noun phrase), VP (verb phrase), PP (preposition phrase) and AP (adjective phrase) groups. A single rule for judging similarity can make grouping items trivial; an example is grouping words based on length (number of characters). Multiple rules for judging similarity are problematic since you are trying to satisfy, in parallel, a number of competing constraints. A spatial representation of structure makes similarity grouping easier to achieve since we can resort to clustering based on a metric such as Euclidean distance (see Chapter 3). For the groupings to be meaningful, though, we rely on the spatial representation carrying some useful information about the structure. Fortunately, RAAM appears to generate representations that convey structural information. Figure 8.7 shows a hierarchical cluster diagram of representations generated using the trees in Figure 8.1. These spatial representations were produced by (S)RAAM (Callan and Palmer-Brown, 1997) which is a mathematical simulation of RAAM, but a conventional RAAM produces similar groupings (see Pollack, 1990). The cluster diagram shows that all but a single tree will fall into a category according to the phrase rule the tree conforms to.

The clustering in Figure 8.7 may be a bit fortuitous, but in general an RAAM will provide some form of similarity-preserving mapping from structure to fixed-width vectors.

The spatial representation of structure is intuitively useful. Inheritance is a structuring technique used both by software engineers and AI practitioners to avoid storing multiple copies of the same knowledge and to provide default reasoning in the event of missing information. Inheritance can be problematic when dealing with exceptions (for example, ostrich does not inherit 'can-fly' from the class bird) and ambiguity when multiple parents contain the same property (which parent should the property be inherited from?). Rules could be provided to handle these problematic situations, but for reasons akin to similarity judgements these rules can be overly constrained because of the symbol-style formalism of these inheritance models. Boden (1996) has used RAAMs in an attempt to overcome problems with exceptions and ambiguity. Boden's approach relies on the spatial representation of object associations.

Structure is conveyed to an RAAM through the timing of presentation of sub-trees to the input layer. One could argue that structure should emerge in a more natural way. For example, when listening to a speaker our senses are picking out a sequence of words that carry no explicit tagging of phrase structuring or word categorization. Elman (1990) has demonstrated that hierarchical categorization can emerge from a sequence. In one experiment, Elman used a simple recurrent network (SRN, see Chapter 5) to discover lexical classes from word order. Templates were used to generate 10 000 two- and

Figure 8.7 Cluster diagram of (S)RAAM representations for syntactic parse trees.

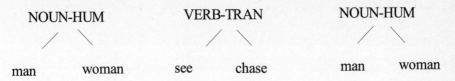

Figure 8.8 Template for generating three-word sentences.

three-word sentence frames. The example frame shown in Figure 8.8 generates three-word sentences (such as 'man see woman'). Each word was coded as a 1-bit-in-31 vector and there were 150 context units. The 27 534 words contained in the 10 000 sentences were concatenated to create a single $(27\,534 \times 31)$-bit vector. Each word was fed to the input layer of the SRN along with the previous context, and the task of the network was to predict the next word in the sequence. The network was trained for six complete cycles of the sequence after which the weights were frozen (so that no more learning took place). The sequence was passed through the network one more time and all hidden unit activations were stored. Each word in the sequence plus context (27 534) was represented by 150-dimensional vectors. Although there were only 29 unique words the 27 534 hidden vectors are expected to be unique because they are superimposed with context information. A summary vector for each word was calculated by averaging all the hidden vectors activated by that word (plus context). These 29 vectors were then grouped using a hierarchical cluster

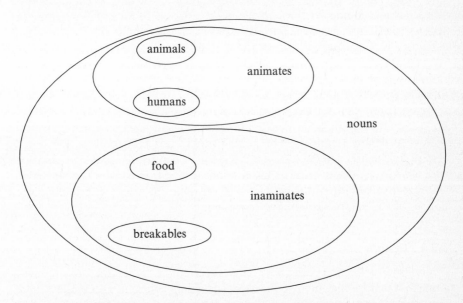

Figure 8.9 Abstraction of a cluster diagram. All representations are nouns; animals and humans are animates, food and breakables are inanimates.

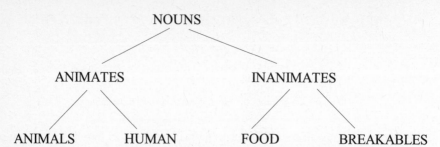

Figure 8.10 Structure reflecting spatial arrangement of nouns from clustering the activations of a simple recurrent network's hidden units. The hierarchy is implicit in that each level in the hierarchy is determined from spatial proximity.

technique. The clustering showed spatial separation of verbs and nouns and also revealed a hierarchical arrangement of word categories, as shown in Figures 8.9 and 8.10.

We are in danger here of overplaying the structural to spatial preservation: that is, structures that are similar end up positioned in similar regions of space. The point was made earlier that it can be difficult to judge whether symbol structures are similar. But the task is only really difficult when we have no criteria for judging similarity. For example, it is trivial to see whether two logic propositions conform to the pattern 'expression ∧ expression'. We look for such patterns to tell whether transformation or inference rules can be applied to a proposition. In this sense, judging similarity is easy because symbol structures are composed through the concatenation of atoms. With numeric vectors, similarity measures appear easy because we could simply state that similarity is judged according to the Euclidean metric. However, using the Euclidean metric to perform, say, clustering is only useful for judging structures as similar provided the vector to which the structure is mapped, maintains information about that structure. The relative spatial location of RAAM representations can, for example, be significantly changed by using arbitrary bit vectors for terminals. Hence, the usual practice of assigning orthogonal bit vectors to denote terminals. The point made in this paragraph is elaborated very well in Sharkey and Jackson (1995). All we can really say is that, usually, with RAAM-style networks, representations can be formed which, if clustered, will reveal something of the character of the data: for example, grouping into nouns, verbs, etc., or grouping by meaning.

8.3.3 Context

Neural networks that distribute and superimpose representations convey context, a feature that many connectionists would proclaim as a major selling point for connectionism. Suppose you have never encountered 'chopsticks' and you happen upon a text with the passage 'They ate spinach with chopsticks'.

You do not know what a 'chopstick' is but by this stage you may start to assume that it is some type of food or possibly eating utensil. Later you read 'The chopsticks were thrown along with the rest of the cutlery into the dishwasher'. So your interpretation of 'chopstick' has shifted from being probably a vegetable to most likely an eating utensil, an inference made possible because you know what a 'spoon' and 'fork' are and 'chopstick' has appeared in the same context. Elman demonstrated this type of conceptual inferencing in the experiment described earlier. When Elman replaced the word 'man' with 'zog' in all 10 000 sentences and presented these transformed sentences to a pre-trained network, the word 'zog' was shown to exhibit the same spatial relationship as the word 'man'.

The type of connectionist network we have been exploring will produce a different representation for the same word appearing in different contexts. For example, 'lemonade' in 'a can of lemonade' will have a different representation than that in a 'bottle of lemonade'. This appears to be a nuisance because a word in a printed symbol form appears as a fixed image irrespective of context (albeit for a change of font or size). The context variability of a representation presents connectionists with a difficult challenge when attempting certain types of computation (for example, structure-sensitive processing, but see below). But on the other hand, it would appear to be a useful feature. Returning to the bottle/can of lemonade example, although 'lemonade' is the same clear liquid whether stored in a can or bottle, some connoisseurs may perceive a difference in taste as being dependent on the type of container from which it is dispensed. We would expect the representation of both 'lemonade concepts' to be very close in semantic space but not exactly the same and so a difference that depends on context seems reasonable.

Kohonen (1990) has also demonstrated the generation of a semantic map of words using a self-organizing map (see Chapter 3). Kohonen generated a set of three-word sentences using a template in a similar manner to Elman (see Section 8.3.2). The sentences were concatenated and a context for each word was defined by averaging over all of its immediate preceding and succeeding words. A vector for each word was then generated by concatenating the word vector code with the surrounding context vector (some of the detail of this composition has been ignored here). The resultant vectors were then used to train a self-organizing map. The semantic map that emerged showed segregation into nouns, verbs and adverbs, and further semantic organization within these regions. Kohonen points out: 'We clearly see that the contexts "channel" the word items to memory positions whose arrangement reflects both grammatical and semantic relationships.'

8.3.4 Symbol versus connectionist representations

Symbols are arbitrary in that one symbol can be replaced with another. If we replace the word TABLE with ZLABET in a passage of text, the reader may find the text a little awkward but still understandable. The symbol TABLE is referring to objects in the world of which the reader has experience and merely changing the label to ZLABET will not affect this experience. Symbols are simply labels and only make sense as representations when utilized by an observer who has a built-in concept (from experience) of what the symbol refers to. In other words, symbols are nothing without the presence of their creators. Symbols are discrete entities and what they refer to is sometimes dependent on surrounding text. For example, 'bark' in 'The bark felt rough' (tree bark) and in 'The bark sounded angry' (a dog's bark) is a discrete symbol but we rely on its links to surrounding text to resolve the concept it is referring to.

In contrast, connectionist representations are not arbitrary, instead they are context-dependent. This intuitively useful feature does pose a difficult question: how many contexts are necessary before a representation is universally useful (for example, for general natural language processing)? An example of the notional difference between a arbitrary symbol representation and one that develops through embedded context can be given. Imagine a collection of fashion models who are registered with a fashion agency. A design house has used all of the models in the past and so the chief designer knows them all by name. The chief designer has a meeting with the agency representative to discuss which models have the look for a coming fashion show. During the meeting all models could be referred to by name or by a photograph. Both a name and a photograph are substitutes for the real thing, but the photograph conveys more useful content because its form is dependent on the real thing it is representing.

Certainly symbol structures are compositional, and processes can be devised that are structure-sensitive. It is hard to perceive of a computing system that does not possess these attributes. Compositionality enables structures to be broken down into sub-parts (possibly for modular processing) and structure-sensitive processing permits a high level of generalization. Suppose we wish to construct the symbol BACKACHE from the symbols BACK and ACHE. If the symbols are held as strings (our computing tokens) then we know that the new symbol BACKACHE is a simple concatenation of BACK with ACHE; at a low level the function *concatenate* will know that BACK has four characters and for the concatenation the new string will have ACHE starting at the fifth character position. Within symbolism, representational tokens such as strings correspond to computing tokens, which allows an explicit algorithm to be written that achieves a desired task (in this case a simple concatenation). Within a connectionist network the computational tokens are unit activations and weight values. The learning algorithms compute input-to and output-from units and update weights. If we were to use an RAAM with 25 hidden units to represent the symbols BACK and ACHE the representations would not lie at the level of computational tokens. Within the RAAM the entire 25 units will be used to represent BACK and to represent ACHE and how to construct BACKACHE is not at all obvious. We could not point to one of the 25 units and state explicitly what that unit stands for (such as B or C, etc.). So, we cannot take the 25 units from the RAAM and state what operation has to be performed on what unit to achieve the concatenation. To perform the concatenation we may resort to what is known as a *holistic* approach. We could, for example, train another feedforward network that would take as input RAAM representations for BACK and ACHE and produce at its output layer an RAAM representation for BACKACHE. We may train the network on hundreds of examples in the hope of deriving a network that will perform the function *concatenation*. The *concatenation* network may generalize correctly when tested on new examples but our confidence that this network will perform correctly on the *concatenation* of any pair of symbols will suffer because we do not know the exact mechanism that the network has employed. A great attraction of symbolism is that, once a function such as *concatenate* has been correctly defined to operate on certain types of computational token, we can be sure, barring human error or hardware fault, that the function will generalize to any tokens whatsoever, provided they are of the correct type.

Although connectionist networks still fall short of symbol processors for tasks such as concatenation, there are a number of demonstrations of holistic processing, eluded to in the previous paragraph that provide a partial response to the criticism that connectionist systems lack systematicity. Remember, for a system to be systematic it should be able to behave as though it understands 'John loves Mary' if it understands 'Mary loves John' or if it understands 'Jane thinks, Mary loves John'. A symbol system can be made to behave in a systematic way within different scenarios. For example, general queries of love relationships can be asked if a system has love(X, Y) as a constituent of any structure (because love is the predicate to be matched and the arguments are variables that can denote any constant). Niklasson and Sharkey (1997) provide an example of structure-sensitive processing with a connectionist system. They showed that logic propositions could be transformed using a connectionist system. For example, $(P \wedge Q) \Rightarrow R$ would be transformed to its logical equivalent $\neg(P \wedge Q) \vee R$.

A ternary RAAM (that is, one with three input fields) with topology 30-10-30 was used to represent 156 propositional formulae of varying complexity. Once the RAAM had been trained half of the 156 RAAM constructed representations were used to train a transformation network to perform transformations of the form

$$(\text{expression} \Rightarrow \text{expression} \Leftrightarrow \neg\text{expression} \vee \text{expression})$$

For example, an input to the transformation network could be the RAAM representation for $(P \wedge Q) \Rightarrow R$ and the target output the RAAM representation for $\neg(P \wedge Q) \vee R$. The transformation network was a standard feedforward heteroassociative network (see Chapter 4). A transformed RAAM representation was decoded back to its constituents using the decoder of the RAAM. The terminal symbols had binary vectors with type tagging as shown in Table 8.3. So, $\wedge$ and $\vee$ are of the same type but, unlike our grammar rules for propositions

Table 8.3 *Orthogonal vectors assigned to terminals*

Terminal	Binary code
P	1000 100000
Q	1000 010000
R	1000 001000
∧	0100 100000
∨	0100 010000
⇒	0010 100000
¬	0001 100000
Nil	0000 000000

in Chapter 7, ⇒ and ¬ are not classed as connectives. The rules governing the syntax of formulae were:

formula → [expression ⇒ expression]
formula → [¬expression ∨ expression]
expression → [atomic|complex]
atomic → [P|Q|R]
complex → [atomic connective atomic]
connective → [∧|∨]

Of the 78 test transformations, all apart from 20 formulae were correctly transformed. In all of the 20 incorrect transformations, the error resulted in a constituent being transformed to a constituent of the same type. This level of generalization is high considering that the transformation network had not been trained on any of the 78 test cases.

It might be suspected that the success of this experiment was due to the type tagging of terminals. To dispel any suspicion the experiment was repeated without any type tagging by encoding all terminals with a random bit vector – 20 bits were used to encode a terminal and the probability that a bit was set to 1 was 3/20. The generalization was slightly better than in the previous experiment.

Another experiment by Niklasson and Sharkey showed that generalization was high even when the transformation network had to cope with other logic transformation laws of the form:

¬(P ∨ Q) transforms to logically equivalent form of ¬P ∧ ¬Q
¬(P ∧ Q) transforms to logically equivalent form of ¬P ∨ ¬Q

Although these connectionist experiments display an impressive level of generalization, they are still deficient in comparison to the systematicity displayed by symbolic transformation rules. Nevertheless, the future of connectionism is promising. Niklasson and Sharkey were able to demonstrate that a connectionist network could learn what symbol types are allowed in certain positions (not simply what symbol tokens are allowed). Generalization of 'type' is an important step towards stronger forms of systematicity. For example, a weak systematic system could generalize love(john, jane) from the set of exemplars {love(john, mary), love(david, mary), love(david, jane)} but a strong systematic system would generalize to love(Human, Human).

Connectionists are beginning to answer criticisms of earlier years, but we should also remember the advantages of connectionist networks in: supporting graceful degradation, fast parallel processing, and context sensitivity. We must also remember that connectionist representations are not arbitrary instantiations but are sensitive to input (that is, what they perceive in the environment). Many AI researches are now arguing that intelligent systems need to evolve through embedding in the environment.

8.4 Natural language processing

8.4.1 Parsing

Reilly (1992) has demonstrated the parsing of sentences. The job of Reilly's parser is to take the category of each word (noun, verb, etc.) one at a time and produce the parse tree of the complete sentence. This dynamic construction of the parse tree from sequences is referred to as *on-line parsing*. For example, 'The boy kicked the ball' has word category constituents D N V D N and a parse tree of ((D N)(V (D N))). The parser is an SRN, and during training the target output will be an RAAM representation of the complete parse tree. The steps involved in parsing a single sentence are shown in Figure 8.11.

Reilly showed that it is possible to build an on-line parser using an RAAM and an SRN. There were problems, however, in getting the system to generalize and training proved somewhat difficult. However, as with any neural models generalization could probably have been improved with a change in training regime. Reilly's main objective was to test the possibility of on-line parsing and consequently the training set was small (16 sequences).

Sharkey and Sharkey (1992) have also built a parser using an RAAM and an SRN. With their model, the SRN was trained to predict the next word in a sequence of words. A three-layer feedforward network was trained to map the SRN hidden unit representations into RAAM representations of the parse tree. When performing, a sentence is read by the SRN to generate a hidden representation; this representation is then mapped to a RAAM representation, which is finally decoded to reveal the phrase structure.

8.4.2 Sentence transformations

Natural language is very expressive and allows the same thing to be said in more than one way. The same message could be conveyed in either the active

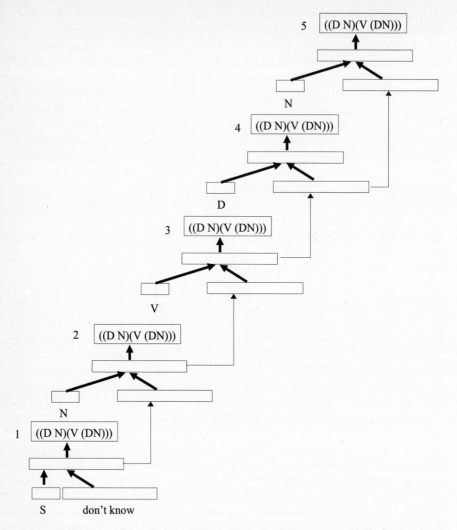

Figure 8.11 The five steps involved in parsing a sentence like 'The boy kicked the ball' using a simple recurrent network. The inputs are word categories and the output is an RAAM representation of the parse tree.

voice or passive voice. For example, the passive version of 'John loves Mary' is 'Mary is loved by John'. Chalmers (1990) has shown that an active to passive transformation is possible using a connectionist system. The set-up is the same as that used by Niklasson and Sharkey for the transformation of logic propositions (see Section 8.3.4) in that an RAAM is used to represent the sentences of both forms and then a backpropagation network is trained to transform the active sentence into its passive form. Chalmers generated

125 sentences and then selected 40 to train an RAAM. The RAAM was trained to represent both the active and passive form of the 40 sentences (that is, 80 sentence representations in total). For a test of generalization, a different set of 40 sentences (80 with both active and passive) were encoded and then decoded. The encoded test representations decoded back to the correct sentence apart from 13. The transformation network was trained using the same 80 sentences that were used to train the RAAM. The 40 RAAM representations of the active sentences served as input and the target outputs were the corresponding 40 RAAM representations in the passive form. At the end of training, the actual passive representations produced on the output layer of the transformation network could all be decoded by the RAAM. Generalization was tested with the 40 sentences used to test the RAAM. Out of the 40 generated passive representations, 26 were correctly decoded by the RAAM.

Although Chalmers said that the generalization rate was better than he had anticipated, he wanted to discover if the failure to generalize on some structures was due to the RAAM or the transformation network. It was noted above that the RAAM failed to give 100% generalization. To eliminate the possibility of the RAAM causing the generalization error, all 125 (250 with both active and passive) of the sentences were used to train the RAAM. The transformation network was then trained with 75 out of the 125 active–passive pairs. The generalization rate was 100% when the transformation network was tested on the other 50 active–passive pairs.

Chalmers also demonstrated that another transformation network could achieve 100% generalization when trained to convert the passive sentence to the active sentence.

Chalmers's experiment shows once again that a connectionist system can be made to perform structure-sensitive processing. Callan and Palmer-Brown (1997) have repeated Chalmers's experiment using the (S)RAAM architecture. The generalization rate of the transformation network was also 100%, but, unlike Chalmers's RAAM, the (S)RAAM did not have to be trained on all sentences. This result is interesting. (S)RAAM is not trained using conventional network techniques such as backpropagation. The training means that (S)RAAM representations are more constrained than RAAM (for example, the number of hidden units is larger) and the fact that (S)RAAM performs well in generalization indicates that the training set is very rich. Although the generalization of the RAAM in Chalmers's experiment was good, it was still less than perfect, and yet the (S)RAAM result would appear to indicate that it should be possible to achieve better generalization with the RAAM. As usual, the full performance potential of a network is often hard to extract.

8.4.3 More complete models

This subsection will look at two connectionist systems that attempt to do a more complete job of language processing. Both systems rely on the idea of scripts.

Scripts are supposed to capture stereotypical situations. With a script, it is possible to fill in missing information from texts like the following:

Julian went with his friends to their favourite Indian restaurant. They ordered the food, along with plenty of water, ate their meal and left a tip before saying goodbye.

From this limited text, and with experience of Indian restaurants, it is possible to answer questions like:

Why did they order plenty of water?
Who served the food?
Who did they leave a tip for?

Most restaurant visits involve a number of standard events such as: entering, being seated by the waiter, selecting a meal from a menu, the order being taken, eating, paying the bill, etc. The script contains roles. There could be roles for the customer, waiter, restaurant name, chef, etc. For a script instance like this one the roles are filled (for instance, Julian plays the role of customer).

The performance of these two models is discussed after they have been introduced.

Script processing with DYNASTY

DYNASTY (DYNAmic STory understanding sYstem) devised by Lee *et al.* (1990), is a modular connectionist system that takes as input a script-based piece of text and produces as output a complete paraphrase. To use an example from DYNASTY's creators, given the input

John entered the Chart-House. John ate the steak. John left a tip.

It produces the following output:

John entered the Chart-House. The waiter seated John. The waiter brought the menu. John read the menu. John ordered steak. John ate the steak. John paid the bill. John left a tip. John left the Chart-House for home.

The operation of DYNASTY centres on distributed semantic representations (DSRs) to represent concepts (for example, milk and man) and propositions (for example, man drinks milk with a straw). The DSRs are generated using extended RAAMs (XRAAMs) that are basically RAAMs with a global dictionary to store symbol–DSR pairs. For example, the symbol 'milk' would be stored with its RAAM representation. A number of modules cooperate to perform the task.

The DSR for a word-concept is produced in such a way that the representation reflects something of the different roles that the word is used in. For example, the role of *milk* in 'the man drinks milk' is subtly different to that in 'the man eats bread with milk': in the first instance *milk* is the main object while in the second *milk* is a co-object. Each of the propositions that milk appears in will play a part in composing the representation of *milk*. Each proposition has an associated case structure. For example, the proposition template

    human ate food with utensil

has the case structure

    AGENT-ACT-OBJECT-INSTRUMENT.

The instance 'man ate spaghetti with a fork' provides case role assignments of [AGENT-man, ACT-ate, OBJECT-spaghetti, INSTRUMENT-fork]. There is a two-way relationship between word-concepts and propositions in that the semantic content of a proposition depends upon each of its word-concepts and each word-concept is dependent upon each proposition the word appears in. Some of this dependence is captured in the way DSRs learn. A concept-encoding network is used to learn word-concepts and a proposition-encoding network is used to learn propositions. Both networks are RAAMs coupled to a global dictionary. The training of both RAAMs is interdependent in that the word-concept network is fed representations formed by the proposition-encoding network and vice versa. During DSR learning all word-concepts are encoded and then all propositions are encoded and the process repeated until stable DSR patterns are obtained (that is, there is no significant change in the hidden unit activations of either network). Word-concepts and propositions are presented to the network as triples. A word-concept is structured as (word-concept, case-role, proposition-label) and a proposition as (proposition-label, case-role, word-concept). Ternary RAAMs are used. For example, suppose the word-concept to be learnt is *milk* and that *milk* appears in the four propositions

p1: The man drinks the milk with a straw.
p2: The company delivers milk in a carton.
p3: Humans get milk from cows.
p4: The man eats bread with milk.

The proposition triples for the word-concept network are

(milk OBJECT p1)
(milk OBJECT p2)
(milk OBJECT p3)
(milk CO-OBJECT p4)

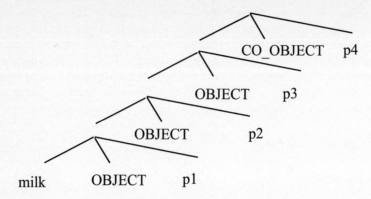

Figure 8.12 The full tree structure for encoding 'milk' in an RAAM. The word 'milk' appears in four propositions.

and the triples for the proposition p1

(p1 ACT drink)
(p1 OBJECT milk)
(p1 INSTRUMENT straw)
(p1 AGENT man)

The tree structures in Figures 8.12 and 8.13 should make clear the way in which the RAAMs are trained.

The learning of DSRs in both networks happens simultaneously. At the start of training the compressed representations for p1 and milk do not exist and so their patterns are set to don't know (all unit values of field 1 are initially set to 0.5). The case-roles (for AGENT, OBJECT, etc.) are fixed as orthogonal patterns.

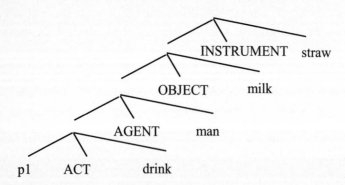

Figure 8.13 The full tree structure for encoding the proposition 'The man drinks the milk with a straw'.

DYNASTY itself contains a number of modules:

1 The DSR learner, consisting of two XRAAM modules as described above.
2 The event encoder, which is a ternary RAAM.
3 The script recognizer, which is a recurrent network that has the task of recognizing the type of script from event sequences.
4 The backbone generator, which is a recurrent network that has the task of generating the complete event sequence.

The event encoder uses a ternary RAAM to represent triples of the form (event, case-role, word-concept). Figure 8.14 shows the input structure for 'John entered Chart-House'. Propositions and events are essentially the same but the networks that form the representations for propositions and events are different. Remember that propositions are represented in the DSR-learning module and the event encoder uses the DSR representations.

The restaurant script roles are:

Script roles: CUSTOMER, RESTAURANT-NAME, FOOD
Instances: John, Jack, Chart-House, Korean-Garden, steak, short-rib

CUSTOMER entered RESTAURANT-NAME
waiter seated CUSTOMER
waiter brought menu
CUSTOMER read menu
CUSTOMER ordered FOOD
CUSTOMER ate FOOD
CUSTOMER paid bill
CUSTOMER left a tip
CUSTOMER left RESTAURANT-NAME for home

If John is substituted for CUSTOMER, Chart-House for RESTAURANT-NAME and steak for FOOD the example script given earlier is produced. The first stage is to learn DSRs for all script roles, the instances used in the training

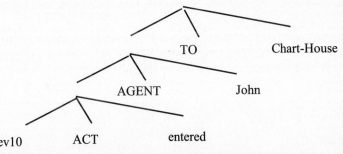

Figure 8.14 The structure for encoding the event 'John entered Chart-House' into an RAAM. The ev number is simply a tag.

scripts and other concepts (menu, entered, etc.). The full set of case-roles is {ACT, AGENT, OBJECT, CO-OBJECT, INSTRUMENT, FROM, TO, LOCATION, TIME}. So for the event

CUSTOMER entered RESTAURANT-NAME

we have

ACT-entered, AGENT-CUSTOMER, TO-RESTAURANT-NAME

Similarly, for

John entered Chart-House

we have

ACT-entered, AGENT-John, TO-Chart-House

To produce the correct paraphrase (that is, the full list of events from the limited subset that is input to the system) DYNASTY has to bind fillers with script roles (for example, John with CUSTOMER). The procedure for role-binding will be examined shortly after a brief look at the script recognizer and the backbone generator.

The job of the script recognizer is to recognize a script (restaurant, shopping, etc.) from a sequence of events. The network operates like an SRN in that the hidden layer activations are fed back to the input layer to act as context. Training is by backpropagation and the training data are taken from several script instances and script types. Script types are denoted by orthogonal patterns and the target output is the script type.

The job of the backbone generator module is to produce the full paraphrase (that is, all events) for a particular script type. So the input to the backbone-generator network is a script type and the output is the full list of events in script-role form (no bindings). For example, the first two events for the restaurant script would be 'CUSTOMER entered RESTAURANT-NAME' and 'waiter seated CUSTOMER'. The network is trained to produce the events as they are represented by the event encoder. The network has a similar architecture to the script-recognizer module. There is a field of units on the input layer to act as context and another field to take the script type.

The DYNASTY process for producing the full paraphrase of a subset of text is as follows:

1 Parse the input text into event-triple form.
2 For each symbol in the event triple, look up the DSR pattern from the global dictionary.
3 Use the event encoder to construct event representations.
4 Use the script recognizer to detect the script type.

5 Generate the complete set of events using the backbone generator.
6 Decode each event from step 5 into event-triple form (using the event-encoder network, that is, the RAAM decoder). This process will break the event representation into its constituent case-roles and DSRs.
7 Do the script-role binding (described next).
8 Look up DSRs in the global dictionary and select their associated symbol.
9 Complete the paraphrase.

The job of the role-binder is to associate script roles with instances. For example, the input to DYNASTY could be:

    John entered Chart-House.
    John ate steak.
    John left a tip.

The first input event triple is (ev10 ACT entered), (ev10 AGENT John) and (ev10 TO Chart-House). The first event from the backbone generator is (ev1 ACT entered), (ev1 AGENT CUSTOMER) and (ev1 TO RESTAURANT-NAME). The input has the same ACT filler (entered) as the first output event triple from the backbone generator and so the script roles are extracted and stored in a binding table. In this instance the two roles (CUSTOMER, John) and (restaurant-name, Chart-House) are stored. The next input event triple is then compared to the next backbone-generated event triple. If the ACT fillers do not match the next backbone event triple is used for comparison. The process repeats until all backbone events are processed. Finally, the script roles in each output event are replaced.

DISCERN

DISCERN (DIstributed SCript processing and Episodic memoRy Network; Miikkulainen, 1994) is one of the most comprehensive language understanding systems developed to date. Like DYNASTY, it is modelled around scripts. An expanded paraphrase of an original story can be produced from a limited text input and DISCERN can also answer questions (for example: What did John eat at MaMaison?). Distributed representation of lexical words (that is, word symbols) serve as the input and output of DISCERN. DISCERN is made up of a number of modules:

Parser

There is a sentence parser that reads words one at a time and produces a representation for each sentence. The story parser creates a representation of the story from the sentence sequences and stores the representation in memory.

Generator

The story generator takes a stored representation and produces a full paraphrase; the sentence generator outputs each word.

Memory

The lexicon is implemented as two feature maps (see Chapter 3). The first map, the lexical map, stores a distributed representation of the symbol form (such as DOG) and the second map, the semantic map, stores a distributed representation of a word's semantics. The distributed patterns of the lexicon capture the visual appearance of a word, and so BALL and DOLL are stored close to each other. The distributed patterns of the semantic map capture the way in which words are used, and so PREY and PREDATOR are stored close to each other. The episodic memory stores the script, track (for example, the restaurant script has fancy food and quick food tracks), and role-bindings.

Story instances are stored as hierarchical feature maps. Scripts are stored in one map which is then connected to a map with tracks which in turn connects to a role-binding feature map. A compressed representation of the story can be used to cue the script map which propagates activity to retrieve the complete paraphrase.

Question answering

The parser builds a representation of a question to cue the episodic memory. The appropriate story representation is generated which the answer module uses along with the question to generate an answer representation which is then fed to the sentence generator.

Tasks such as parsing and answer generation are performed with hierarchically organized FGREP (Forming Global Representations with Extended backPropagation; Miikkulainen and Dyer 1991) modules. FGREP modules are basically three-layered backpropagation networks. The inputs and outputs of these networks are stored in the lexicon. If an FGREP module processes a sequential input or output, the hidden-layer activations are saved at each stage and then fed back to the hidden layer along with the next item in the sequence. The cue-former and answer-producing modules use non-recurrent FGREP networks; the parsers and generators are recurrent, with the former taking sequential input and the latter producing sequential output.

The input and output layers of an FGREP module are split into fields, the number of fields being dependent on the particular module's task. A non-recurrent FGREP could be trained to map the syntactic constituents of a sentence to case roles. The fields on the input layer would denote the syntactic constituents {Subject, Verb, Object, With} and the output layer the case-role constituents {Agent, Act, Object, Instrument, Modifier}. An example mapping is shown in Figure 8.15.

Each field in the input and output layer is loaded with the lexicon entry for the word. During training the lexicon entries are continually changing. Initially the lexicon starts with random entries which change during training, before eventually stabilizing once training is complete. The representations are changed at the input layer using extended backpropagation. Unlike standard backpropagation which would only calculate errors for the hidden units to

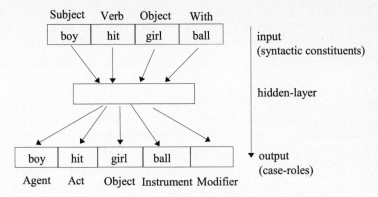

Subject	Verb	Object	With
boy	hit	girl	ball

input
(syntactic constituents)

hidden-layer

boy	hit	girl	ball	

Agent   Act   Object Instrument Modifier

output
(case-roles)

Figure 8.15 The mapping of syntactic categories onto case-roles.

adapt the first layer of weights, FGREP goes a step further and calculates errors for the input units. The activation at an input unit is then changed according to the product of its error signal and a learning rate. The essence of the technique is to treat the input representations as an additional layer of weights.

The sentence parser uses a recurrent FGREP with a single input field (because one word is read at a time) and an output field for each case-role. The story parser has an input field for each case-role and an output filled for the script type, the track, and each script role. The output of the sentence parser serves as input to the story parser.

The paraphrase of an input story follows a number of steps:

1 The lexical representation of each word is presented to the lexical map which in turn produces the semantic representation from the semantic map.
2 The semantic representations are fed one at a time to the semantic parser. At the end of a sentence the case-role representations are fed to the story parser.
3 The story parser takes a sequence of sentence representations from the sentence parser and produces a complete representation of the whole story on the output layer. Instances from the story will now be bound to roles.
4 The story representation is fed to the episodic memory which extracts (classifies) the story's script, track, and role-bindings. The complete story representation (full paraphrase) is retrieved from the weight vectors of the competition-winning units in the script, track and binding layers.
5 The story generator takes the story representation and generates a sequence of case-role sentences.
6 The sentence generator takes each sequence from the story generator and outputs each word (in its semantic representation).
7 Finally, the lexicon is used to convert the semantic representation of a word into its lexicon form.

A question can be parsed into a case-role representation which the cue former takes to produce an approximate story representation. The episodic memory is then cued for the script, track and role-bindings which are then used to generate an answer.

Performance of DYNASTY and DISCERN

Both models were shown to perform well at generalization. For DYNASTY, Lee *et al.* (1990) used four scripts (restaurant, taking a lecture, shopping and visiting a doctor) and generated eight instances of each. Out of the 32 script instances, 16 were used for training and 16 for testing generalization. All training and test scripts were processed correctly. Miikkulainen tested DISCERN with 96 stories instantiated from three scripts and three tracks. Out of the text generated, 98% of the words were correct. Clearly both systems performed well.

DISCERN is really a more complete connectionist model compared to DYNASTY in that the parser, for example (for DYNASTY), was not implemented but left for future work. Central to the performance of both systems is the mechanism for forming representations, and here both use a similar recirculation method. The FGREP representations formed in the DISCERN model are learned while the system is learning to perform its task, whereas the DSRs in DYNASTY are formed independent of the task. While it can be argued that FGREP representations are tuned to the task at hand, DSRs, having been learned independent of the task, should be portable to other tasks requiring access to word content (see Lee *et al.*, 1990). Overall, both models perform well at what is essentially the same task and both provide good examples of how modular architectures are developing.

Miikkulainen (1995) describes another modular architecture, SPEC (Subsymbolic Parser for Embedded Clauses), for processing sentences with embedded clauses (for example, 'The girl, who liked the dog, saw the boy'). SPEC is designed to parse sentences with novel combinations of clause structures not seen during training. The central component is the now familiar SRN which maps a sequence into a case-role representation. This SRN parser is augmented with an RAAM implemented stack to store clauses (for example, 'The girl') for later consideration during the parse and a feedforward segmenter network that breaks a sequence into clauses.

8.5 Some further points regarding representation

8.5.1 Generalization

'Generalization' is quite a wide-ranging term. We perform pattern generalization effortlessly. For example, you can recognize a friend's face even when he changes his appearance by growing a beard or changing his hair style. Generalization can also refer to something more abstract. For example, we do not have to be explicitly told that an object with an undercarriage of attached wheels will be easier to push than one with no wheels; we can learn this for ourselves. The experience of pushing various types of object enables us to induce the relevant knowledge such that when we see a new object for the first time, we can make a good guess as to its resistance to being pushed. The knowledge with respect to the usefulness of wheels must somehow be abstracted from the whole object because wheeled objects can be very different in appearance: we cannot always point to an object and say that it is similar to some other object and therefore it will be easy to push. Also, the presence of wheels alone is not good enough for the generalization: many objects, designed to be stationary, have wheel-type creations. Abstracting knowledge should make the knowledge portable. For instance, an engineer knows that a supermarket trolley should be designed with wheels and we can work out that a washing machine will be easier to move if we place rollers underneath it. The knowledge of wheels exists in a form that makes it available to a wide range of scenarios.

Barnden (1992) has put the case for explicit generalization. Connectionists have mainly concentrated on implicit generalization. For example, a network could be trained to map examples of specific communists living in a town to 'atheist'. The system could be trained to generalize so that for any communist in the town it outputs the activity pattern representing 'the person is an atheist'. What the system has not done is to construct the generalization that 'all or most communists living in the town are atheists'. Suppose the explicit generalization is to feed a system that is to apply the rule:

If all (or most) communists living in a town are atheists then the town is eligible for a grant from the Fundie Fund.

Barnden's example highlights the difference between generalization to specific instances and generalization over a class. The eligibility for the Fundie Fund, requires generalization over a class.

Suppose you grow up not knowing what a cup of tea is and suddenly people (who assume you have had tea before) start offering cups of tea when you visit. After a while you will know that the cup of brown liquid just placed in front of you is likely to be hot (you have also been served a few cups of cold tea). You can generalize that 'most cups of tea are served hot'. The explicit generalization makes the knowledge portable. You could, for instance, recognize an association with the statement 'buy this tea cosy if you like your tea hot'.

It is easy to see why many pragmatists argue for hybrid systems – systems that take advantage of both the symbol and connectionist paradigms. 'Hybrid' has become somewhat difficult as a term because it means different things to different people. For some, a hybrid system contains distinct modules that can be identified as either symbolic or connectionist. At the other extreme, the

PUT DOVE

Figure 8.16 The character ⅃ might be read as a u or v depending on the context in which it is shown.

synthesis might be more integrated within an architecture such as RAAM which is a connectionist model designed to represent symbol structures. We can ignore the level of hybridization and examine why the idea is an attractive one.

Consider context. Is the symbol 'ᴠ' a 'v' or a 'u'. The recognition of the symbol will not necessarily pose a problem because we may be able to resolve the confusion when given context. In Figure 8.16, the symbol is interpreted as a 'u' in PUT (there is little difficulty if the symbol PUT is taken to be a word). Is the second word DOVE or DOUE? Additional context (say, if the word is part of a sentence) may resolve the ambiguity. We might consider resolving letter ambiguity using a hybrid approach: construct a neural network to select a number of possible candidates (for example, 'u' or 'v') and use symbolic rules that encode word and sentence structural knowledge to settle on a final candidate. In this case the neural network examines a single character and the rules resolve the contextual information. Alternatively, we could envisage solving the complete task with a neural network. The task in fact seems very suited to a connectionist approach because it involves pattern recognition, for which neural networks are good, and we know that representation of context comes naturally to neural networks. But there comes a point where for higher-level processes we need a mechanism whereby knowledge can be abstracted, and this is still a difficult issue for connectionists.

An ability to abstract is necessary for solving complex tasks. Through abstraction we can suppress detail and concentrate resources on the essential elements of a task. Whether we are designing a building or planning a holiday, we work first with minimal detail to keep the workload manageable, before adding more information in stages. Abstraction appears to be fundamentally linked to language. Consider the statements:

Animals have skin.
Animals breathe.
Animals eat.

These statements are abstracted from observing many creatures within our world. Through these statements knowledge is made portable for use in a number of contexts. For example, you would not have to know what a dog is, if you were told that it is an animal, to conclude that keeping such a creature would require food to be supplied. It is not necessary for you to have ever seen a real dog for you to know a good deal about it.

Language is a very rich form of communication when used between humans. Through language, we might prescribe a pattern of behaviour in a fellow being by issuing an instruction, we can participate in games with complicated rules, and, as we have seen, we can pass on knowledge. Symbol systems are language systems. All computer scientists would like an easy facility for embedding knowledge in a machine. We see this through successive generations of programming languages, from machine code to higher-level languages. We crave systems that are easier to program. At present, for most systems, humans have to solve the given task and then communicate the solution to a machine through a programming language. The appeal of machines that learn, such as connectionist machines, is that the program comes as a by-product of the machine learning to solve the task. We will, however, never extract the full potential from machines until we can communicate with them. Even a limited form of communication, in terms of the machine reacting to instructions, for example, could be a good step forward. In the next subsection, the notion of symbol grounding is introduced, which might prove essential for machines to have true understanding and an ability to communicate. This is followed by a brief examination of two connectionist systems that provide some insight into how machine communication might be realized.

8.5.2 The symbol grounding problem

Harnad (1993) states:

> Cognition cannot be just computation, because computation is just the systematically interpretable manipulation of meaningless symbols, whereas the meanings of my thoughts don't depend on their interpretability or interpretation by someone else.

According to Harnad, symbol capacities have to be grounded in robotic capacities.

Earlier in this chapter we spoke of symbols being meaningless entities in themselves which can only convey meaning when interpreted by an agent (restricted to ourselves at present) that already understands what the symbols mean. Equipping a machine to perceive and interact with its environment gives the machine the potential to work out for itself an understanding of objects and events in the world. Harnad thinks that neural networks might be a candidate for grounding symbols.

In Harnad *et al.* (1994) it is noted that people see objects differently when they learn to sort them into categories. Objects of the same category seem more alike and those of a different category look more different. Harnad *et al.* used a backpropagation network to demonstrate the formation of such categories where objects had a spatial category representation in terms of the hidden unit activations. According to the authors, such categories can be given symbol labels, and these symbols can be combined into strings to form propositions about objects. According to the authors:

> The meanings of such symbolic representations would be 'grounded' in the system's capacity to pick out from their sensory projections the object categories that the propositions were about.

We can use an earlier example of Harnad's (1990) to try and make the grounding idea clearer. Suppose a robot operating in the world learns to discriminate a category for those objects we know as 'horse' and another category for those we know as 'stripes'. If these categories are labelled 'horse' and 'stripe', then the symbols 'horse' and 'stripe' would be grounded. A grounded symbol for 'zebra' could then be formed from 'zebra = horse & stripe'.

Harnad's approach is hybrid. We can imagine a neural network connected to sensory apparatus. After observing many objects in the real world, there is a region in the network's representation space where everything we know as a 'horse' lies, and similarly for 'stripes'. The connectionist part is perceiving and categorizing. The categories can then be labelled with symbols and new symbols generated by combining with other symbols. Symbols such as 'zebra = horse & stripe' are composed symbolically but the symbol 'zebra' is supposed to be grounded because it is composed out of categorical representations.

Sharkey and Jackson (1994) are uncomfortable with this hybrid approach. To use two of their examples: imagine a horse with thin stripes running along its back or a horse standing next to a barber's pole (a pole with red stripes): would you call such compositions a zebra? No, of course not, and yet both objects would be compositions of the form 'horse & stripes'.

The context dependence of connectionist representations, which we often take to be extremely useful, seems in another sense to be problematic. Consider the notion of 'coffee'. 'Coffee' has a representation that depends on context. 'Coffee' in a jar would be a different representation (albeit similar in some sense) to 'coffee' in a cup. How might we identify the notion of 'coffee' to make it portable for some other use? Symbols are portable because they are discrete, arbitrary and not context-dependent. Perhaps we need a context-independent component for connectionist representations? Sharkey and Jackson (1994) take the hidden unit activations of a feedforward network to be context-dependent but take the weights as a context-independent representation. To see this idea, consider an RAAM that represents 'cup of coffee' and 'jar of coffee'. 'Coffee' in both statements has a different representation because it is composed with 'cup' in the first instance but 'jar' in the second. However, there will be one or more units on the input layer to denote the symbol 'coffee' and once an RAAM has learned, the weights connecting the coffee input units to the hidden layer remain fixed. Nothing other than the symbol 'coffee' sends an excitory signal along these weights and the signal remains the same for all instances of 'coffee', irrespective of the context 'coffee' appears in. The weights therefore can be taken as a context-independent representation. So instead of grounding 'cup of coffee' as equal to 'coffee & cup' using categorical labels, the context-independent weights for 'coffee' and 'cup' are used to form a context-dependent composition for 'cup of coffee' on the hidden units.

The notion of symbol grounding could prove to be crucial for the development of truly intelligent systems. Returning to the notion of 'wheels', how does one completely describe all that there is to know about 'wheels'? Where does the knowledge about 'wheels' end? Do we not learn more about objects as we progress through life? If, however, we cannot capture in a neat package all the knowledge about wheels, how can that knowledge be made available for use in different scenarios? Perhaps Harnad's ideas, and those of Sharkey and Jackson and others, provide us with a way forward!

8.6 The possibility of machine communication

In this section we will look at two systems that provide some insight into how communication with a machine might be developed. We should stress that fluent communication with a machine is a long way from being realized, but there is no reason not to expect some useful developments over the next few years. There already exist intelligent Web agents that take instructions in English to search for documents. These agents though, at present, are a mere glimpse at what should be possible in the future.

The authors whose work is presented in this section were not primarily concerned with demonstrating machine communication *per se*, but we can take a look at their work from a communication perspective.

Nenov and Dyer have developed DETE (see Nenov and Dyer, 1994; or, for a summary, Dyer, 1994). DETE is designed to perceive and interact with a limited environment. DETE is equipped with an eye to perceive blobs that are free to move on a visual screen and a finger with which to push or touch the blobs. During learning there are three forms of information: frames from a screen representing stationary or moving blobs; sequences of motor commands (for example, move the eye); and verbal descriptions of the visual/motor sequences. After learning, DETE can provide a verbal description of a visual/motor sequence, or alternatively can generate a sequence of visual/motor representations from a verbal description.

Visual and motor features are associated with words/phrases. For example, the command 'Touch big green square' is a command to the finger to interact with an object that has feature values big, green and square. DETE's world, although limited, is rich in terms of possible spatial-temporal associations. For instance, a square may be to the left of a triangle blob, moving from left to right on the screen, and at some stage the square could overtake the triangle if travelling faster. The word 'overtake' is an association between blobs that is dependent on the variation of spatial location over time.

screen

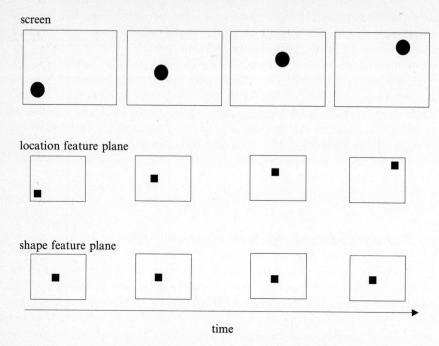

location feature plane

shape feature plane

time

Figure 8.17 An example of DETE feature frames. Associated with the motion frames of the screen are a series of feature frames that describe how the feature varies (if it does) over time.

Nine feature frames, each consisting of a two-dimensional array of 16×16 units, are used to represent the visual/motor events. Four contiguous units within each feature frame are used to represent a blob. For a particular blob, a feature may be variant or invariant. For example, the circle in Figure 8.17 is moving from the bottom left-hand corner of the screen to the top right-hand corner. The circular blob in this case stays the same shape and size, and moves at the same speed. The feature planes for shape, size and speed will have the same set of units activated over each time frame, but different units in the location feature frame will be activated as the circle moves across the screen.

More than one blob can be present on the visual screen at the same time. Different blobs are assigned different activation phases in the feature planes to overcome the possibility of 'visual cross-talk' (for example, if a large triangle and a small square are present simultaneously, the system, without phasing, could not tell the actual objects from the small triangle and the large square).

For verbal input, a simplified phonemic representation is used. Basically, a 64-bit string is used where each bit represents the presence or absence of a frequency value. Phonemes are repeated so that the verbal duration matches the time that a blob is present on the visual screen. To learn the meaning of 'ball moves', the utterance 'ball moves' is played for different video sequences where features such as size and speed, etc., are allowed to vary but the shape and motion feature planes are invariant (because the ball is always round and is always moving for it to be described as 'ball moves').

DETE has a number of memory modules, each module being a neural architecture known as 'katamic memory'. Katamic memory is a complicated architecture designed to learn sequence associations and perform sequence completion if given a sub-sequence as a cue. There is a memory module for each feature plane that is designed to code a memory trace of the activity coming from the corresponding feature plane.

DETE learns in stages: single words are learned first followed by word pairs, gradually building up to longer word sequences. DETE could generalize to novel sequences of words seen during learning. DETE was also trained to answer simple questions by performing sequence completion. The training consisted of sequences containing a question word and answer word within a visual context. For example:

"what_size" (visual scene: large green triangle)?, answer "large"
"what_colour" (visual scene: small red ball)?, answer "red"

DETE also learned motor sequences. For instance, DETE could be shown two blobs and be given the verbal input "what_is_bigger" to which it would respond by selecting the relevant blob with its eye and generating a verbal response.

Noelle and Cottrell (1995) have also explored the association of linguistic output with perception. Their approach was very simple. The network architecture consists of two SRNs, as shown in Figure 8.18. The output layer produces a linguistic description of a perceived event that has been presented to the scene layer. The scene layer receives sequences of simple pixel representations (only two pixels high and four pixels wide) of a ball, rolling, flying or bouncing across a screen. A linguistic token is produced at each time step and so a description like 'ball bounces right' would be generated over three consecutive time steps. A movie image is presented to the scene layer at each time step. When a verbal description is required, the activations of the movie sub-network are frozen, and the description sub-network is run for three cycles to produce the linguistic output.

Noelle and Cottrell's motivation was to demonstrate that linguistic strings could be intrinsically related to some domain task. This notion, along with the idea that a connectionist system could exhibit systematic performance (as demonstrated by their adder network, presented in Chapter 5), formed the basis for the idea of an instructable network – that is, a network that could respond appropriately to some simple instruction sequences. Noelle and Cottrell's experimental set-up was very simple and the domain task not

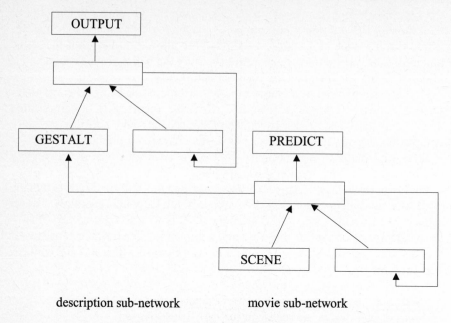

description sub-network   movie sub-network

Figure 8.18 Noelle and Cottrell's use of two SRNs trained to associate linguistic output with simple image sequences.

particularly interesting, but their intention was to highlight the potential utility of an instructable network and to demonstrate that it is feasible. There have been a number of approaches to embedding prior knowledge into a neural network in order to kick-start learning. Noelle and Cottrell's idea is interesting because it integrates conventional neural learning with 'learning by being told'. A successful implementation of such a system could lead to a dynamically adaptive system: When you want the system to change its response, you tell it so! The ability to communicate via language with a network could also be useful in testing a system's performance: if the system responds quickly and correctly to an instruction then the system must have the appropriate embedded knowledge. Also, as Noelle and Cottrell point out, such a system might help cognitive scientists explain high-level reasoning processes and how these processes emerge from simpler associational mechanisms. Noelle and Cottrell experimented with a number of architectures, but we shall take a brief look at only the first of these.

At a basic level, training a network to respond to instructions is no different than any other form of training. One could, for example, encode instructions as patterns which are then spliced with the training data (that is, instructions are concatenated with instances of training patterns). It is cleaner, though, from an engineering point of view, to keep the instructions separate from the input data.

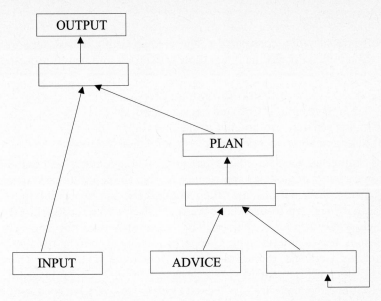

Figure 8.19 Illustration of the instructional network used by Noelle and Cottrell.

Also, it is desirable to have a facility for feeding variable-length instructions, and this is made easier if the instructions and data are kept separate.

Noelle and Cottrell experimented with a discrete mapping task. Examples are: mapping A to B or C to A, etc. Instructions take the form of a sequence such as $\Rightarrow AB$, which is an instruction telling the network to map the input A to the output B. A sequence of instructions could be fed to the network such as $\Rightarrow AB \Rightarrow CC \Rightarrow BC$, which states that A should be mapped to B and both C and B should be mapped to C. A moment later, the instruction could change to $\Rightarrow AA \Rightarrow BB$, which requires the network to map A to A and B to B while C is left open to map to anything.

The network model is shown in Figure 8.19. For a trained network, instructions are fed to the advice layer where activation is propagated only as far as the plan layer. When the complete instruction sequence has been fed in, the activation values in the plan layer are frozen (stay fixed) and used as constant modulating input to the mapping sub-network. Any input presented during modulation should produce an output that conforms to the instruction. A phased training strategy is used where the number of instructions is gradually incremented. An instruction is presented, the plan layer is frozen, and the network is then trained on each instance for which an instruction is relevant.

The accuracy of training was 98% and generalization was 96%. This result was improved later, by using a modified architecture.

8.7 Summary

This chapter has only considered a few of the existing neural network links to AI. Sun (1995) divides the integration of symbols and neural processes into four categories:

1 specialized localist networks for symbol processing;
2 symbol processing in distributed neural networks;
3 combining separate symbol and neural networks;
4 embedding neural network elements in symbol architectures.

In this chapter we have considered category 2 (though much has been left out) and some aspects of modular approaches. Within the connectionist community distributed representations are often emphasized but there are those who believe that local representations have a significant role to play in the quest for high-level cognitive machines. That there is a need for connectionists to account for high-level symbol-style processing is not in question. This account must address compositional and systematic capabilities. There is a sense in which neural network research has come full circle in the last decade. The much cited volumes by McClelland *et al.* (1996) were largely aimed at the construction of cognitive and biological models. The fact that the majority of connectionist literature is engineering-oriented is testimony to the utility of connectionist models. There is now a new emphasis on building connectionist models for higher-level intelligent processes. Indeed, Arbib (1995) stated that 'we need many such books'.

8.8 Further reading

A detailed account of FGREP and DISCERN can be found in Miikkulainen (1993). A collection of papers on connectionist natural language models can be found in Reilly and Sharkey (1993); for an overview of hybrid connectionist natural language processing, see Wermter (1995). There are a number of volumes that look specifically at symbol connectionist links. Some of the models discussed in this chapter can be found in these volumes. The chapters in these volumes were written by active researchers and include applications, theoretical issues and philosophical discussions. These volumes were edited by: Dinsmore (1992), Honavar and Uhr (1994), Sun and Bookman (1995) and Dorffner (1997). Clark (1993) is highly recommended for a discussion of key issues.

8.9 Exercises

1 A RAAM is to be used to encode the following tree:

((A B)(C B))

(a) Sketch the tree.
(b) List all sub-trees.
(c) List a set of suitable vectors for the terminals.
(d) Suggest an initial RAAM architecture.

2 Repeat Question 1 for the following tree:

((A (F G))(B ((C D) E))).

3 Repeat Question 1 for the following tree:

(A ((B C D) A E) NIL).

4 For the tree listed in Question 2:
(a) List the way in which the sub-trees are encoded.
(b) List the way in which the sub-trees are decoded.

5 Repeat Question 4 for the tree in Question 3.

6 Given the following templates and propositions listed below:

Proposition template	Case-roles
Human kicked the object	AGENT-ACT-OBJECT
The object moved	OBJECT-ACT
Human hit human with the hitter	AGENT-ACT-OBJECT-INSTRUMENT

P1. John kicked the ball.
P2. John hit David with the ball.

(a) List the word-concept triples and the proposition triples for an XRAAM.
(b) Sketch the trees, for the triples developed in (a), that show their encoding structure for an XRAAM.

7 Repeat Question 6 with the additional proposition

P3. The ball moved.

8 A neural network exists with five binary units. If a unit represents something it outputs 1 and if it does not take part in a representation it is set to 0. How many local representations can the network encode and how many distributed?

9 Words can be considered as made up of terminals (the letters) filling specific roles. For example, the word BAR has B at role 1, A at role 2 and R at role 3. We may consider words as being more visually similar the more role

fillers they have in common. For example, TAR could be considered more similar to BAR than it is to RAT. Explain how this similarity might be affected if the terminals are denoted using arbitrary binary vectors instead of orthogonal ones. Illustrate your explanation with an example.

10 Does an SRN differ from a sequential RAAM (that is, one designed to represent sequences)? Explain.

Some linear algebra

An ordered pair of numbers can be regarded as a point or a vector in two-dimensional space, as shown in Figure A.1. A two-dimensional point is said to be a member of $\mathbb{R}^2$, a three-dimensional point a member of $\mathbb{R}^3$ and an n-dimensional point a member of $\mathbb{R}^n$. A vector in $\mathbb{R}^n$ is written using the notation $\mathbf{x} = [x_1 \ x_2 \ \ldots \ x_n]$. The elements may or may not be delimited by commas. A vector can be written in row format or column format. For example,

$$\mathbf{x} = [1 \quad 3 \quad 2]$$

is in row format, while

$$\mathbf{y} = \begin{bmatrix} 1 \\ 3 \\ 2 \end{bmatrix}$$

is in column format. Because the element values and order are the same for both $\mathbf{x}$ and $\mathbf{y}$, $\mathbf{y}$ is the transpose of $\mathbf{x}$, written as $\mathbf{y} = \mathbf{x}^T$, or $\mathbf{x}$ is the transpose of $\mathbf{y}$, written as $\mathbf{x} = \mathbf{y}^T$.

Addition of vectors

Vectors can be added or subtracted. The procedure follows our usual understanding of addition and subtraction on an element-by-element basis:

$$\mathbf{x} = [1 \quad 3 \quad 2]$$
$$\mathbf{y} = [1 \quad 6 \quad 5]$$
$$\mathbf{x} + \mathbf{y} = [2 \quad 9 \quad 7]$$
$$\mathbf{x} - \mathbf{y} = [0 \quad -3 \quad -3]$$

Multiplication by a scalar

A vector can be multiplied by a scalar. For example, multiplying $\mathbf{x} = [1 \ 3 \ 2]$ by 2 produces a vector twice as long, $2\mathbf{x} = [2 \ 6 \ 4]$.

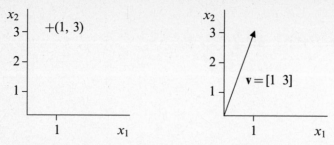

Figure A.1 The same member of $\mathbb{R}^2$ viewed as a point on the left and a vector on the right.

The norm of a vector

The *norm* or *magnitude* of a vector is

$$\|\mathbf{v}\| = \sqrt{v_1^2 + v_2^2 + \cdots + v_n^2}$$

So, for the vector, $\mathbf{x} = [1\ \ 3\ \ 2]$, the norm is

$$\|\mathbf{x}\| \sqrt{1^2 + 3^2 + 2^2} = \sqrt{14}$$

Dot product

The dot product of the two vectors $\mathbf{v} = [v_1\ \ v_2\ \ \ldots\ \ v_n]$ and $\mathbf{w} = [w_1\ \ w_2\ \ \ldots\ \ w_n]$ is

$$\mathbf{v} \cdot \mathbf{w} = v_1 w_1 + v_2 w_2 + \cdots + v_n w_n$$

Also

$$\mathbf{v} \cdot \mathbf{w} = \|\mathbf{v}\|\|\mathbf{w}\|(\cos \theta)$$

where θ represents the angle between the two vectors.

EXAMPLE

Find the dot product of the vectors $[-1\ \ 3\ \ 6\ \ -2]$ and $[1\ \ 2\ \ 2\ \ -3]$. Find the angle between the two vectors.

SOLUTION

The dot product is

$$[-1\ \ 3\ \ 6\ \ -2] \cdot [1\ \ 2\ \ 2\ \ -3]$$
$$= -1 \times 1 + 3 \times 2 + 6 \times 2 + -2 \times -3 = 23$$

The angle between the two vectors is

$$\cos \theta = \frac{23}{\sqrt{50}\sqrt{18}}$$

$$\theta = 39.94°$$

Two vectors are *perpendicular* or *orthogonal* if their dot product is zero. To see this, observe that if $\cos \theta = 0$ then θ is 90°.

Matrices

A matrix is a rectangular array of numbers. An $m \times n$ matrix is a matrix with m rows and n columns. Each element of a matrix can be indexed by its row and column position. The order of elements is written thus:

$$\mathbf{A} = \begin{bmatrix} a_{11} & a_{12} & a_{13} & \cdots & a_{1n} \\ a_{21} & a_{22} & a_{23} & \cdots & a_{2n} \\ a_{31} & a_{32} & a_{33} & \cdots & a_{3n} \\ \vdots & & & & \\ a_{m1} & a_{m2} & a_{m3} & \cdots & a_{mn} \end{bmatrix}$$

For the 3×2 matrix $\mathbf{B}$, given below, the element $b_{32} = -5$ and $b_{21} = 3$:

$$\mathbf{B} = \begin{bmatrix} -2 & 1 \\ 3 & 4 \\ 2 & -5 \end{bmatrix}$$

Matrix multiplication

To multiply two matrices, $\mathbf{A}$ and $\mathbf{B}$ (written as $\mathbf{AB}$), the number of columns in $\mathbf{A}$ has to match the number of rows in $\mathbf{B}$. If $\mathbf{A}$ is an $m \times n$ matrix and $\mathbf{B}$ is an $n \times s$ then the matrix product $\mathbf{AB}$ is an $m \times s$ matrix. If $\mathbf{C} = \mathbf{AB}$, then an element of this product is defined as

$$c_{ij} = (i\text{th row vector of } \mathbf{A}) \cdot (j\text{th column vector of } \mathbf{B})$$

$$c_{ij} = \sum_{k=1}^{n} a_{ik}b_{kj}$$

EXAMPLE

Compute the product

$$C = \begin{bmatrix} -2 & 3 & 1 \\ 1 & 2 & 4 \end{bmatrix} \begin{bmatrix} 4 & 2 & 1 & 1 \\ -3 & -1 & 4 & 3 \\ 1 & 4 & 5 & 1 \end{bmatrix}$$

SOLUTION

The elements c_{11} and c_{23} are calculated thus:

$$C = \begin{bmatrix} -2 \times 4 + 3 \times -3 + 1 \times 1 & \cdots & \cdots & \cdots \\ \cdots & \cdots & 1 \times 1 + 2 \times 4 + 4 \times 5 & \cdots \end{bmatrix}$$

and the complete solution is

$$C = \begin{bmatrix} -16 & -3 & 15 & 8 \\ 2 & 16 & 29 & 11 \end{bmatrix}$$

Matrix transpose

If the matrix B is the transpose of matrix A, then the element b_{ij} is the same as element a_{ji}.

EXAMPLE

Write the matrix B if $B = A^T$ and

$$A \begin{bmatrix} -2 & 3 & 1 \\ 1 & 2 & 4 \end{bmatrix}$$

SOLUTION

$$B = \begin{bmatrix} -2 & 1 \\ 3 & 2 \\ 1 & 4 \end{bmatrix}$$

Matrix addition

Matrices can be added by summing likewise elements. For example, if $C = A + B$, then $c_{ij} = a_{ij} + b_{ij}$.

Representing a graph with matrices

A matrix can be used to represent a graph of weighted paths as shown in Figure A.2.

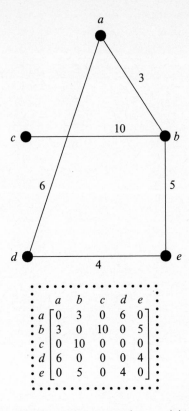

Figure A.2 A matrix representing a weighted graph.

Applying vector and matrix notation to neural networks

In the summary of Chapter 2 an example of a forward and backward pass
through a feedforward network using the backpropagation algorithm is given.
The example is given in diagram form (Figure 2.22) so that the reader can
confirm the calculations. The diagram is given again (as Figure A.3) for convenience. The backpropagation algorithm, like all other network algorithms, is
expressed using concise mathematical notation. There is really nothing difficult
about the calculations, but the algorithms can be a little intimidating
if you are not familiar with the notation. Probably the most difficult part of the
notation is relating the subscripts written in the equations to the network units
and weights.

For the backpropagation algorithm, the input to a unit is given as

$$net_j = w_0 + \sum_{i=1}^{n} x_i w_{ij}$$

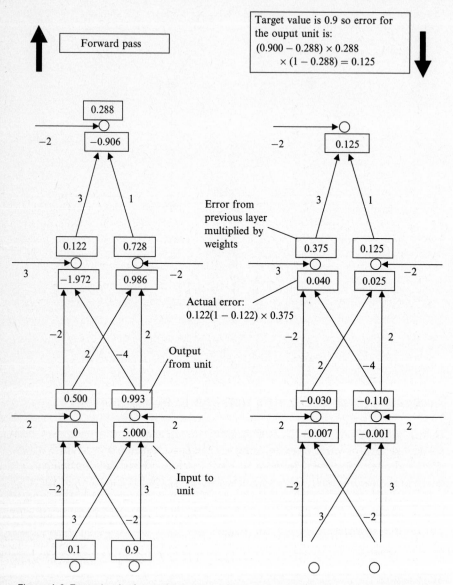

Figure A.3 Example of a forward pass and a backward pass through a 2-2-2-1 feedforward network. Inputs, outputs and errors are shown in boxes (see Figure 2.21).

where x is a signal being sent from another unit and w is the weight connecting the other unit to the current unit whose input we are calculating. The number of units sending signals is n. The variable w_0 is the bias weight that can be considered as connected to a unit whose output signal is always fixed at 1, and so we can rewrite the input as

$$net_j = \sum_{i=0}^{n} x_i w_{ij}$$

In the example at the end of Chapter 2, the first layer's of weights are

$$\mathbf{W}_1 = \begin{bmatrix} 2 & 2 \\ -2 & 3 \\ -2 & 3 \end{bmatrix}$$

The first row gives the bias weights connecting to the first and second unit of the first hidden layer. Including the bias unit, there are three input units on the input layer and hence the matrix has three rows and two columns for the two hidden units. There is a bias unit on the hidden layer, but since the bias unit is never connected to units in the previous layer it does not appear in the weight matrix.

When a forward pass is made, the j indexes the unit whose input we are calculating and the i indexes a unit in the previous layer. If we present the input [0.1 0.9] to the network, the inputs to the first two hidden units are given as the product

$$\begin{bmatrix} 1.0 & 0.1 & 0.9 \end{bmatrix} \begin{bmatrix} 2 & 2 \\ -2 & 3 \\ -2 & 3 \end{bmatrix} = \begin{bmatrix} 0 & 5 \end{bmatrix}$$

The input vector is prefixed with 1 since this is the value that the bias unit always sends out. So the net input to the first unit is 0 and to the second is 5. If we calculated the output for these using the sigmoid function we could prefix the output vector with 1 and take the product of this vector with second layer of weights to give the inputs to the units in the second hidden layer. In this case, j would now index the current units whose input we were calculating in the second hidden layer and i would index the units in the first hidden layer.

In the backpropagation algorithm the error of a hidden unit is calculated during the backward pass. The error of a hidden unit depends on the errors of the units to which the hidden unit feeds signals during the forward pass according to:

$$\delta_j = o_j(1 - o_j) \sum_{k=1}^{n} \delta_k w_{kj}$$

Since j indexes the current unit whose error we are calculating, o refers to the activation (output) for the current unit. The layer of units sending back their errors is indexed by k. The second layer of weights in our example is

$$\mathbf{W}_2 = \begin{bmatrix} 3 & -2 \\ -2 & 2 \\ -4 & 2 \end{bmatrix}$$

Since error signals are being sent back in the direction that is the reverse of the forward pass, to calculate the product $\sum \delta_k w_{kj}$ we have to transpose the weight matrix. Remember that k indexes the units that are sending back the errors. The errors for the two units in the last hidden layer have been calculated as [0.040 0.025]. So the product of the errors feeding into the units of the first hidden layer can be calcuated thus:

$$[0.040 \quad 0.025] \begin{bmatrix} -2 & -4 \\ 2 & 2 \end{bmatrix} = [-0.03 \quad -0.11]$$

Note that the first row of the weight matrix $\mathbf{W}_2$ has been removed for the backward pass because we do not calculate an error for a bias unit. We do not need an error for the bias units because the error of a unit is used to update the weights that impinge on a unit during the forward pass, and of course no weights impinge on a bias unit.

Glossary

Activation	In this text, the signal that a unit sends out, to either other units or the environment.
Activation function	Function used to calculate a unit's activation from its input.
Arc	A link connecting two nodes in a graph data structure.
Association	*See* Autoassociation, Heteroassociation.
Autoassociation	Autoassociative learning can be used to memorize patterns that can later be recalled using noisy versions of those memorized patterns. The object is to recover the clean version.
Batch updating	Where weights are adapted after all patterns have been presented. Error terms are accumulated for each pattern and the weights adapted at the end of a single iteration. Although it is typical to update after all patterns have been presented, the batch size can be made to vary.
Centroid	The average location of all patterns within a cluster. The centroid is found by taking the average of all the pattern vectors.
Cluster	Group of patterns that are located close together.
Compositional structures	Structures that can be constructed from other structures. Tree structures are an example. Each tree is made up of sub-trees.
Connectionist	Artificial neural networks are often referred to as connectionist networks, and the paradigm of neural networks is often referred to as 'connectionism'. Some scientists are interested in artificial neural networks as a tool in helping to understand the neural networks in our own brain. 'Connectionist' is sometimes used to emphasize that neural nets are being used for the purpose of computing with no concern for biological realism.
Distributed representation	Where more than one unit is used to represent a concept. Also a single unit will take part in representing more than one concept. A local representation uses a single unit to represent a concept (for instance, dog).

Epoch	A single iteration through all patterns.
Feature	A variable (or attribute). For example, a person's height and weight are both features.
Feedforward network	A network whose connections all lie in the same direction from the input layer to the output layer.
Font	Uses a number of attributes to define the appearance of characters on an output device such as a video screen.
Generalization	A term used to refer to how well a network performs on data on which it has not been trained. For instance, a supervised network with good generalization would be expected to classify correctly the majority of test cases. There are slightly different interpretations of generalization depending on the context of the discussion, but the explanation given here is the most commonly used interpretation.
Global minimum	When a network's parameters (weights and/or activations) are set so that the average squared error or energy is at its lowest. The global minimum represents an optimum solution. Local minima are regions with a low error or energy but do not represent an optimal solution.
Heteroassociation	Similar to association, except that a pattern is associated with a different pattern as opposed to being associated with itself.
Hidden units	Units that do not connect to the environment.
Learning rate	A parameter that is usually set to a constant value before training. This parameter controls the amount by which a weight can change during a single update.
Local minima	*See* Global minimum.
Local representation	*See* Distributed representation.
Mapping	Has a strict mathematical definition, but less formally refers to the process that transforms an input pattern to an output pattern.
Momentum	A constant term used during backpropagation learning. The momentum controls the effect of a previous weight change on the current weight change. This parameter helps prevent the weight changes oscillating and can help in avoiding local minima.
Network model	Used to refer to different types of neural network. Different models can vary in the learning algorithm, the way in which units connect and the way in which units update.
Neuron	*See* Unit.
Node	*See* Unit.

Pattern	Refers to a data record that is presented to a network. Also referred to as a (training or test) instance. For example, it might be the binary pixel elements that describe a printed character, or a person's personal details given when applying for a bank loan.
Pattern of connectivity	Refers to how the network units are connected (wired) to each other.
Pattern updating	Where weights are adapted after each pattern is presented.
Pixel	The smallest element that can be written to a video screen. The higher the number of pixels (dots), the greater the resolution.
Recurrent network	A network that has weights that serve to feed back signals. For example, signals that a unit receives from other units could be processed and the activation fed back to those units that sent the original signals.
Semantic space	Patterns that have similar meaning lie in the same region of pattern space (that is to say, their vectors are located close together).
Supervised learning	A type of learning that can be applied when it is known to which class a training instance belongs. With supervised learning we know what the network should produce as output for each training instance. If the network does not produce the correct output then the learning algorithm uses this information to adjust the network (usually by adapting the weights).
Symbolism	A term used to refer to the way in which traditional artificial intelligence attempts to model the world. Knowledge is represented as symbol structures. For example, a symbol could be a word that denotes a single concept like 'dog' or it could be made more complex into an object with attributes (has fur, barks, eats meat).
Topology	For a network, this term refers to the way in which the network's units connect.
Training	The procedure used to get a network to learn a task from exposure to data.
Unit	The simple processor element of a neural network that connects to many other units via weights. Other terms used are node, neuron and neurode.
Unsupervised learning	Learning that is used when the training instances do not have a known class.
Weight	A connection between two units. Some units connect to themselves. A connection has a real number value called its strength which is used to excite or inhibit signals

travelling along the connection. A weight is defined by having a start unit (from which it emerges), an end unit (where it terminates) and a value denoting its strength.

Weight matrix

The matrix is used to list the weight values (strengths) that exist in the network. The position of a weight within the matrix will define which units the weight connects. Sometimes, more than one weight matrix is used to describe the way in which the units are connected in a network. For example, if units are placed in layers then a single matrix might be used to describe the connections between two layers.

References

Ackley, D.H., Hinton, G.E. and Sejnowski, T.J. (1985) A learning algorithm for Boltzmann machines. *Cognitive Science*, 9: 147–169.

Arbib, M.A. (1995) Foreword, in R. Sun and L.A. Bookman (eds), *Computational Architectures Integrating Neural and Symbolic Processes, A Perspective on the State of the Art*. Boston: Kluwer Academic Publishers.

Barnden, J. (1992) Connectionism, generalization, and propositional attitudes: A catalogue of challenging issues, in J. Dinsmore (ed.), *The Symbolic and Connectionist Paradigms, Closing the Gap*. Hillsdale, NJ: Erlbaum.

Baum, E.B. and Haussler, D. (1989) What size net gives valid generalization? *Neural Computation*, 1: 151–160.

Boden, M. (1996) A connectionist variation on inheritance. Paper presented to the International Conference on Artificial Neural Networks 96, Bochum, Germany.

Broomhead, D.S. and Lowe, D. (1988) Radial basis functions, multi-variable functional interpolation and adaptive networks. Royal Signals and Radar Establishment, Malvern. Memorandum 4148.

Callan, R. and Palmer-Brown, D. (1997). An analytical technique for fast and reliable derivation of connectionist symbol structure representations. *Connection Science*, 9(2): 139–159.

Carpenter, G.A. and Grossberg, S. (1987) A massively parallel architecture for a self-organizing neural pattern recognition machine. *Computer Vision, Graphics, and Image Processing*, 37: 54–115.

Cawsey, A. (1998) *The Essence of Artificial Intelligence*. Hemel Hempstead: Prentice Hall.

Chalmers, D. (1990) Syntactic transformations on distributed representations. *Connection Science*, 2(1/2): 53–62.

Clark, A. (1993) *Associative Engines. Connectionism, Concepts, and Representational Change*. Cambridge, MA: MIT Press.

Cleeremans, A. (1993) *Mechanisms of Implicit Learning, Connectionist Models of Sequence Processing*. Cambridge, MA: MIT Press.

Copeland, J. (1993). *Artificial Intelligence, A Philosophical Introduction*. Oxford: Blackwell.

Dean, T., Allen, J. and Aloimonos, Y. (1995) *Artificial Intelligence*. Redwood City, CA: Benjamin/Cummings Publishing Company, Inc.

Dinsmore, J. (ed.) (1992) *The Symbolic and Connectionist Paradigms, Closing the Gap*. Hillsdale, NJ: Erlbaum.

Dorffner, G. (ed.) (1997) *Neural Networks and a New Artificial Intelligence*. London: International Thomson Computer Press.

Dyer, M.G. (1994) Grounding language in perception, in V. Honavar and L. Uhr (eds), *Artificial Intelligence and Neural Networks. Steps toward Principled Integration.* London: Academic Press.

Elman, J. (1990) Finding structure in time. *Cognitive Science,* 14: 179–211.

Fausett, L. (1994) *Fundamentals of Neural Networks. Architectures, Algorithms and Applications.* Upper Saddle River, NJ: Prentice-Hall.

Fodor, J. and Pylyshyn, Z. (1988) Connectionism and cognitive architecture: A critical analysis. *Cognition,* 28: 3–71.

Geman, S. and Hwang, C.R. (1986) Diffusions for global optimization. *SIAM Journal of Control and Optimization,* 24: 1031–1043.

Harnad, S. (1990) The symbol grounding problem. *Physica D,* 42: 335–346.

Harnad, S. (1993) Symbol grounding is an empirical problem: Neural nets are just a candidate component, in *Proceedings of the Fiftieth Annual Meeting of the Cognitive Science Society.* Hillsdale, NJ: Erlbaum.

Harnard, S., Hanson, S.J. and Lubin, J. (1994) Learned categorical preception in neural nets: Implications for symbol grounding, in V. Honavar and L. Uhr (eds), *Artificial Intelligence and Neural Networks. Steps toward Principled Integration.* London: Academic Press.

Haykin, S. (1994) *Neural Networks, A Comprehensive Foundation.* New York: Macmillan College Publishing Company.

Hecht-Nielsen, R. (1990) *Neurocomputing.* Addison-Wesley Publishing Company, Inc.

Hinton, G.E., Plaut, D.C. and Shallice, T. (1993) Simulating brain damage. *Scientific American,* October.

Honavar, V. and Uhr, L. (eds) (1994) *Artificial Intelligence and Neural Networks. Steps toward Principled Integration.* London: Academic Press.

Hopfield, J.J. (1984) Neurons with graded response have collective computational properties like those of two-state neurons, in *Proceedings of the National Academy of Sciences,* 81: 3088–3092. Reprinted in J. Anderson and E. Rosenfeld (eds) (1988) *Neurocomputing: Foundations of Research.* Cambridge, MA: MIT Press, pp. 579–584.

Jordan, M.I. (1989) Serial order: A parallel, distributed processing approach, in J.L. Elman and D.E. Rumelhart (eds), *Advances in Connectionist Theory: Speech.* Hillsdale, NJ: Erlbaum.

Kohonen, T. (1990) The self-organizing map. *Proceedings of the IEEE,* 78(9): 1464–1480.

Kosko, B. (1988) Bidirectional associative memories. *IEEE Transactions on Systems, Man and Cybernetics,* 18: 49–60.

Kremer, S.C. (1995) On the computational power of Elman-style recurrent networks. *IEEE Transactions on Neural Networks,* 6(4): 1000–1004.

Lee, G., Flowers, M. and Dyer, M. (1990) Learning distributed representations of conceptual knowledge and their application to script-based story processing. *Connection Science,* 2(4): 313–345.

Lippmann, R.P. (1987) An introduction to computing neural nets. *IEEE ASSP Magazine,* 4: 4–22.

Masters, T. (1995) *Advanced Algorithms For Neural Networks. A C++ Sourcebook.* New York: Wiley.

Miikkulainen, R. (1993) *Subsymbolic Natural Language Processing, An Integrated Model of Scripts, Lexicon, and Memory.* Cambridge, MA: MIT Press.

Miikkulainen, R. (1994) Integrated connectionist models: Building AI systems on subsymbolic foundations, in V. Honavar and L. Uhr (eds), *Artificial Intelligence and Neural Networks. Steps toward Principled Integration.* London: Academic Press.

Miikkulainen, R (1995) Subsymbolic parsing of embedded structures, in R. Sun and L.A. Bookman (eds), *Computational Architectures Integrating Neural and Symbolic Processes, A Perspective on the State of the Art.* Boston: Kluwer Academic Publishers.

Miikkulainen, R. and Dyer, M.G. (1991) Natural language processing with modular neural networks and distributed lexicon. *Cognitive Science*, 15: 343–399.

Nenov, V.I. and Dyer, M.G. (1994) Perceptually grounded language learning, Part 2: DETE: A neural/procedural model. *Connection Science*, 6(1).

Niklasson, L. and Sharkey, N.E. (1997) Systematicity and generalization in compositional connectionist representations, in G. Dorffner (ed), *Neural Networks and a New Artificial Intelligence.* London: International Thomson Computer Press.

Noelle, D.C. and Cottrell, D.C. (1995) Towards instructable connectionist systems, in R. Sun and L.A. Bookman (eds), *Computational Architectures Integrating Neural and Symbolic Processes, A Perspective on the State of the Art.* Kluwer Academic Publishers.

Norris, D. (1989) How to build a connectionist idiot (savant). *Cognition*, 35: 277–291.

Pollack, J. (1990) Recursive distributed representations. *Artificial Intelligence*, 46: 77–105.

Reilly, R. (1992) Connectionist technique for on-line parsing. *Network*, 3, 37–45.

Reilly, R.G. and Sharkey, N.E. (eds) (1993) *Connectionist Approaches to Natural Language Processing.* Erlbaum.

Rumelhart, D.E., Hinto, G.E. and Williams, R.J. (1986a) Learning Internal Representations by Error Propagation, in Rumelhart *et al.* (1986b), *Parallel Distributed Processing, Explorations in the Microstructure of Cognition.* Vol. 1, Foundations. Cambridge, MA: MIT Press.

Rumelhart, D.E., McClelland, J.L. and the PDP Research Group (1986b) *Parallel Distributed Processing, Explorations in the Microstructure of Cognition.* Vol. 1, Foundations. Cambridge, MA: MIT Press.

Russell, S. and Norvig, P. (1995) *Artificial Intelligence, A Modern Approach.* Hemel Hempstead: Prentice Hall.

Sharkey, N.E. and Sharkey, A.J.C. (1992) A modular design for connectionist parsing, in *Twente Workshop on Language Technology 3: Connectionism and Natural Language Processing.* Enschede, The Netherlands: Department of Computer Science, University of Twente, pp. 87–96.

Sharkey, N. & Jackson, S. (1994). Three horns of the representational trilemma, in V. Honavar and L. Uhr (eds), *Artificial Intelligence and Neural Networks. Steps toward Principled Integration.* London: Academic Press.

Sharkey, N.E. and Jackson, S.A. (1995) An internal report for connectionists, in R. Sun and L.A. Bookman (eds), *Computational Architectures Integrating Neural and Symbolic Processes, A Perspective on the State of the Art.* Boston: Kluwer Academic Publishers.

Specht, D.F. (1990) Probabilistic neural networks. *Neural Networks*, 3: 109–118.

Sun, R. (1995) An introduction: On symbolic processing in neural networks, in R. Sun and L.A. Bookman (eds), *Computational Architectures Integrating Neural and Symbolic Processes, A Perspective on the State of the Art.* Boston: Kluwer Academic Publishers.

Sun, R. and Bookman, L.A. (eds) (1995) *Computational Architectures Integrating Neural and Symbolic Processes, A Perspective on the State of the Art*. Boston: Kluwer Academic Publishers.

Werbos, P.J. (1990) Backpropagation through time: what it does and how to do it. *Proceedings of the IEEE*, 78(10): 1550–1560.

Weijters, A., Van Den Bosch, A., Van Den Herik, H.J. (1997) Behavioral aspects of combining backpropagation learning and self-organising maps. *Connection Science*, 9(3): 235–251.

Wermter, S. (1995) *Hybrid Connectionist Natural Language Processing*. London: Chapman & Hall.

Index